The Better Sleep Blueprint

Parenting is a lifelong journey.
I hope this book helps
you navigate the
early months/years!

Jennifer

x

The Better Sleep Blueprint

Jemma Munford

BROWN DOG BOOKS

Published under licence by Brown Dog Books and
The Self-Publishing Partnership Ltd, 10b Greenway Farm, Bath Rd,
Wick, nr. Bath BS30 5RL

www.selfpublishingpartnership.co.uk

ISBN printed book: 978-1-83952-673-2
ISBN e-book: 978-1-83952-674-9

Cover and internal design by VCM Graphic Design
Printed and bound by CPI Group (UK) Ltd, Croydon, CR0 4YY

This book is printed on FSC® certified paper

MIX
Paper | Supporting
responsible forestry
FSC
www.fsc.org
FSC® C013604

For Max and Holly,

Who made me a mum.

And Mark for your unwavering support (and patience).

Table of Contents

Introduction 6

CHAPTER 1.. 10

Why is Baby Sleep so Bloody Hard? 10

CHAPTER 2.. 14

Attachment and Parenting Style 14

CHAPTER 3.. 21

The Science Bit.. 21

CHAPTER 4.. 37

Temperament.. 37

CHAPTER 5.. 47

Unsettled Babies... 47

CHAPTER 6.. 56

Safe Sleep 56

CHAPTER 7.. 59

The DNA Method.. 59

CHAPTER 8.. 63

D is for Daytimes.. 63

CHAPTER 9.. 66

Naps... 66

Troubleshooting Naps 75

CHAPTER 10.. 85

N is for Night times 85

CHAPTER 11 ....**97**

A is For Sleep Associations......................................97

Sleep Strategies 111

CHAPTER 12...**123**

Sleep Problem Symptom Checker............................123

CHAPTER 13...**126**

Common Early Years Challenges 126

CHAPTER 14...**145**

Biologically Normal Sleep in the first Two Years....................145

CHAPTER 15...**156**

All About You 156

To Conclude 180

Recommended Books..183

Recommended Resources...184

References 185

Introduction

"Breathe Jem, breathe, please!"

I could hear the words in the distance, muffled at first but as I concentrated on that instruction, they became clearer and louder. It was my husband, Mark kneeling next to me in bed in the pitch black whilst holding our crying baby.

I was having a panic attack in the middle of the night because for the 5th (15th or 500th!) time that night, I had been woken up again by our baby (baby number 2).

It had been a year or more of multiple night wakings, being woken up as soon as my head hit the pillow at bedtime and being screamed at by this tiny person who just wouldn't give up and just... bloody... sleep. I felt like I was losing my mind.

The next day, I refused to get up, I didn't want to be a mum any longer, I was done.

In reality, it wasn't that I didn't want to be a mum, I had post-natal depression (PND) and I was absolutely exhausted thanks to the relentlessness of never being able to relax and rest.

Thankfully with lots of support from my ever reliable and kind husband, I was able to recover from PND and we were able to use my knowledge as a qualified sleep consultant to find a way to move forwards.

And that's why I wrote this book.

I, probably like you, knew that I would be tired when I had my baby, after all I'd had numerous unhelpful comments like "get your rest in now while you can!" or "say goodbye to sleep for the next few years" but I didn't really have the faintest idea of just how bloody hard it would really be, or the huge impact it would have on my mental health, my physical health and my relationships.

Tiredness as a parent is more than just needing an early night, you are exhausted, overwhelmed and juggling so many new hats. You don't have the energy or mindset to be the fun, happy and attentive parent you dreamed of being. You feel like you're just doing a rubbish job at everything – parenting, relationships with your spouse or friends, and you don't feel like you're effective at work anymore. You live your life through a fog, unable to string sentences together, feeling hungover every day without the fun of a good night out! This tiredness is all consuming!

Luckily (please detect my sarcasm here), I had some great advice thrown at me "she just needs to learn to go to sleep by herself, she'll stop crying eventually" (they didn't know my daughter!), "you're making it worse by going to her" or one of my favourites "she's just crying for you, so you'll go to pick her up" (no shit, Sherlock!)

Despite my mental health challenges and absolute exhaustion, I still didn't want to sleep train my children that way. What I knew about attachment and the benefits of responsive parenting meant that even if I had wanted to leave her to cry it out to get more sleep, I simply couldn't follow it through (and don't get me wrong, on more than one desperate occasion I tried!).

I'm a sleep consultant who qualified with some of the most well-known names in the sleep, neuroscience, and parenting world (Lyndsay Hookway, Gordon Neufeld, and Dr Laura Markham to name a few). I'm also a mum of two myself with one wonderful sleeper and one who quite honestly nearly finished me off! But no matter how hard it got - and it did, I hit rock bottom, I never doubted my instinct to respond to my children when they needed me (even though there were many times that I wanted to run away and hide).

I wrote this book to share with you all the things I wish I had known about baby sleep before I became a parent. For me, knowledge is confidence and reassurance. If I understand the ins and outs of something, then I feel happier knowing I made an informed choice. I feel better able to ignore the white noise of unsolicited advice, I'm happy and secure in my plan to move forwards in a way that works for me and my family.

Throughout this book, I'm going to help you to understand how baby sleep works and give you a plan of how to make positive changes to get better sleep without needing to leave your child to cry by themselves.

I'm also going to explain what else is important to your growing and developing child, and you might be surprised to know, it's not just about how much sleep they get.

It's not going to lecture you on attachment parenting and how you should give over your whole life, bed, and soul to your baby, but it will give you a plan of how to parent responsively with a balance of considering your own needs as well as the needs of your developing child.

There is no judgement here, you may have purchased this book after trying the traditional sleep training methods I mentioned above. Maybe they worked but then you needed to do it again when your child was older and this time it isn't working.

Maybe you have a child who can't be left to cry for any length of time as they vomit (this was my daughter!), or because you have another child who you don't want to be disturbed in the night.

Maybe you're here because those extinction and separation-based methods simply don't align with your parenting style, and sitting on the landing outside listening to your baby's cries is just unbearable.

Whatever brought you here, know that baby sleep is really bloody hard to cope with, it is not a measure how good a parent you are, and there are very few families where they are not finding the pressures of modern life adding to the overwhelm with even 'normal' baby sleep.

You will sleep again; you can feel better about it all and by finding your responsive parenting pathway to improve sleep, you will look back and be proud that you did things the way you wanted to.

Jem x

CHAPTER 1

Why is Baby Sleep so Bloody Hard?

P arenting, in some respects could be considered easier than before, we have so much technology at our fingertips to support our everyday challenges, from apps to track feeds and sleep, white noise machines, and even machines to make the 'perfect' instant bottle of formula.

The reality though is that parenting nowadays is more difficult than ever, let's think about why.

Many parents are having children in later life, so have less energy to keep up with them and cope with sleepless nights. I also found that having children later in life (I was 36 when I had Max) I certainly felt that I'd lost a huge part of myself and my independence, having had total freedom for so long!

Many more mums are managing jobs and careers alongside raising children for financial security.

You have probably heard the phrase **'it takes a village to raise a child'** and it is so true. Only 50-100 years ago did we live in a society where we had a community of friends and family who were on hand to offer support and advice. Now we are juggling lives where we may not live close to our families anymore, thanks to starting a family later, we may even be responsible for caring for our parents, and we are often trying to manage busy jobs and social lives. Even if we live close to family, many more grandparents are now working full time into their sixties and seventies and therefore are not as available to help out as they would have been a generation or two ago.

Financial worries are more common, we need to take parental leave at significantly reduced earnings and the cost of childcare is extortionately high. It is no wonder parents find raising a family so difficult now. With the cost of living being as it is, very few families can afford to live off only one wage, meaning that often both parents have to work outside of the home, whether they would choose to or not.

Not only do we have the stresses and strains of personal family life but there is the added pressure of society's perception and opinion about our parenting styles and choices.

"Congratulations is he good?".

"Sleeping like a baby".

"Ooh you're making a rod for your own back".

"Are they sleeping through yet?".

"Is he good??" This was one of the questions I used to hear when I had my first baby, often from total strangers in the street or supermarket. Has anyone ever asked you this question? How do you define 'good' with regards to a baby? Is he robbing any banks yet? Stealing any cars? What is a 'bad' baby? The undertone of this is really asking does he cry a lot? Does he sleep well? Now of course babies cry and don't sleep a lot, which is absolutely normal, but does it make your baby 'bad'?

"Are they sleeping through?" …or "Do they sleep for you?" is also a common question, why? Why does it matter to someone else whether your baby sleeps through or not? As though this a measure of parental success or how 'good' your baby is? Like a badge of honour, you can wear once they sleep through the night.

And of course, if you ever confess that they're not sleeping through yet, you're often met with pity, or given unsolicited advice about how you could do it better. And if you dare admit you do anything to support your baby to fall asleep, you'll be warned that 'you're making a rod for your own back!"

And let's face it, whoever came up with the phrase "sleeping like a baby" needs finding and asking what they were thinking! Did you expect your baby to sleep quietly and be still and settled for quite long periods? Were you surprised when your baby arrived, and he or she wriggles, grunts, sighs, breaks wind, and startles themselves awake?

These are just a few examples of what expectations society sets around baby sleep and they are just not accurate. What else are we told that makes us feel like our baby is broken or we are doing something wrong, and where do these ideas come from in the first place?

Why Do We Think This?

Humans are 'carry mammals', our babies are born the most dependent (as opposed to 'cache mammals' like rabbits who can be left in the nest whilst the mother goes in search of food). Our milk is the lowest in fat and protein compared to other mammal's milk, so it makes sense that our babies need to stay close to us for warmth and to feed very regularly to survive.

Just based on that alone, it's hardly surprising that our babies don't want to sleep separately from us and can't sleep all night without feeding.

Unfortunately, evolution hasn't yet been able to send babies the memo that there aren't any woolly mammoths coming to scoop them up from the cave floor as soon as they are placed down out of our arms, so it's also not surprising that babies want to be held a LOT.

We have only really moved away from the biologically normal way of viewing children's sleep in the last 100 years. Before then it was common that we would bedshare and mothers would always keep babies with them.

It is totally normal for immature mammal babies to sleep for short periods, waking lots overnight and to wanting to be close to us.

The change in perception of normal infant sleep came from two popular (in their day) psychologists who shared their views back in the 1920's. These opinions have unfortunately influenced how many people view infant sleep since.

John B Watson and Frederick Truby King said things like:

"No child could have too little affection, for example, Truby King capped cuddles to no more than 10 minutes per day."

"A 'good baby' preferred solitary confinement in his pram in the backyard."

"Crying is important for children."

It is such a shame that some of these ideas do still linger on in our society; nothing about how our child sleeps (or doesn't sleep for that matter) is the fault of the parent, nor is it babies who are somehow manipulating parents into providing comfort (I mean, God forbid they need comfort!)

The idea that crying is important for a baby or that it is possible to give too much affection is extremely harmful - not to mention the safety implications of leaving a baby to sleep alone in the garden for hours at a time! All these skewed ideas of what children need cause problems with attachment, and to raise a healthy, well-adjusted child, believe it or not, attachment is even more important than sleep.

CHAPTER 2
Attachment and Parenting Style

I chat to many parents who are worried about sleep who also worry about attachment in one way or another. Typically, they worry that by responding to their babies in the night, or by supporting them to sleep, they are somehow creating bad habits which need to be squashed otherwise they will create a spoiled, lazy, and dependent child. Or that by doing these things, they'll need to do them for years to come and will never get a break from it.

I hear it, it's totally relatable, but remember we've all had it drummed into us that our children needing us is somehow bad and add to that we're all knackered thanks to our busy modern lives, the thought of needing to be there for our children in the long term can feel scary and overwhelming.

It's helpful though to understand how attachment works, how the brain develops, and this is where you're going to feel so confident in telling those people who give you awful advice like 'just leave them to cry' to take their advice and …. You know what.

Attachment in its definition by John Bowlby (a pioneering psychologist) is "a lasting psychological connectedness between human beings". Babies enter the world instinctively programmed to form attachments as this will help them to survive.

You begin the process of attachment even before your baby is born. You may have given your baby a name in the womb, followed the updates of what size vegetable they compare with during pregnancy and begun imagining your life with the little being you haven't even met yet.

Babies also connect with us before birth: they hear our voices, and it has even been proven that they respond to a familiar song or sound that they heard in utero.

This connection is built upon in the early months and years and emotional availability, attunement and responsiveness is an important part of helping your child to build a secure attachment.

The Importance of Secure Attachment

Attachment is so important in your child's development as it affects how they develop physically, mentally, emotionally, and socially. It can even be a key indicator of how well they will do in later life! (Gaertner et al., 2008).

To form a secure attachment, children need to be dependent whilst developing and experiencing the world to be able to become independent humans. This need for dependency should not be taken lightly, we are in a powerful position as parents to help our children to be capable of reaching their full potential in life.

Adults with a secure attachment tend to have better relationships (Mikulincer, 1998) are more competent and have higher self-esteem (Wu, 2009).

Having a secure attachment gives your baby the feeling of being protected and that they can depend on you to support their needs. It gives your child the confidence to be able to explore the world more independently because they are assured of your support and response.

Children who have a secure attachment tend to be more independent (Hong & Park, 2012), be more compliant with their caregivers (Mark et al 2002), do better academically (Moss & St Laurent, 2001), have less anxiety and be more socially confident (Di Tommaso et al 2000 & Bohlin at al 2000).

But how do we support a secure attachment? We have the power to support and shape our baby's brain by the way we choose to parent.

Your Baby's Brain in Your Hands

When we are born, the human brain is around 30% the size of a fully formed adult brain. By aged 5 it has grown and developed to around 90%.

What is fascinating about the brain is that we are born with all the brain cells we'll ever have but the connections between those cells (neurons) are not fully formed. It is these connections (synapses) that make your brain work the way it does (and your brain will work differently to mine).

These connections are formed faster in early childhood than at any other time in our lives. At age 2-3, there are more connections than in adulthood (Conel, 1963), however, to make the brain more efficient, it will prune away the connections hardly used and strengthen the ones used more frequently.

The brain will form these synapses through life and emotional experiences, so that it can adapt to the environment appropriately. For example, a baby growing up in a stressful environment will be wired to cope with that stress by focusing on heightened threat and defence impulses.

By adapting our parenting style to be responsive, calm, and attentive to our child's needs, we are supporting optimal brain development.

How we parent literally shapes how the brain forms, laying the foundations for how we think, feel, and react to stress for the rest of our lives.

The brain has two emotional systems – **Alarm** and **Calm/Social**.

The alarm system has **Rage, Fear** and **Panic/Grief** networks.

The calm/social system has **Care, Seeking** and **Play** networks. (There is also Lust later in life!)

These systems work like muscles, so if one system is activated more than another, then that system will lead (Sunderland, M. 2007).

Our brains are made up of higher and lower regions. The lower region is like other mammals, and this area mostly thinks in the present. This part of the brain controls the alarm system, so when we feel unsafe or under threat, it drives us to respond with impulsive fight or flight reactions, anger or behave anxiously (Morgane, Galler & Mokler, 2005)

The higher part of our brain is bigger than other mammals. Here we can use imagination and reasoning/problem solving skills and control our impulses. The challenge is that sometimes the instinctive lower brain can take over the functions of the higher brain, which as Margot Sunderland explains in her book 'What Every Parent Needs to Know' means we can sometimes behave like a threatened animal.

What we must remember is that our child's upper and lower brain regions are not very well connected, which is why they can't rationalise and manage their emotions. This is why they have a huge stress response to the fact you gave them a blue cup instead of the red one, that they've lost their dummy, or they are over stimulated. Think how stressful the world must be when you haven't all the life experience you now have as an adult.

They are not being naughty or manipulative, they quite literally can't behave any other way right now. If your child's arousal system has been triggered, YOU are the only way they can calm and regulate.

The Urban Child Institute says:

"Early brain development is the foundation of human adaptability and resilience, but these qualities come at a price. Because experiences have such a great potential to affect brain development, children are especially vulnerable to persistent negative influences during this period.

On the other hand, these early years are a window of opportunity for parents, caregivers, and communities: positive early experiences have a huge effect on children's chances for achievement, success, and happiness."

It makes sense that the movement towards more responsive, attuned parenting is only going to support future generations in realising their human potential! How cool is that?!

Responsive Parenting

Emotionally responsive, attuned parenting can set the tone for how your baby's brain handles stress. By consistently offering support and comfort in times of upset, stress and dysregulation, the brain will form pathways that make it easier for them to cope with the same stressors as they get older.

Without support to calm and regulate, the brain can be 'wired for hyper-arousal' where they are never able to relax and be calm (Moore, 2009). Comforting your child helps strengthen their vagus nerve, which runs from the brain to other major organs like the heart and gut.

It regulates the functions of the digestion, heart rate and immune system. Having a strong vagal tone means your body can relax faster after stress.

But how can we be responsive to our young children, when we're not always sure of what they need?

If they are unhappy, mirror their expression to show you understand then offer comfort through touch like a hug.

It's also about giving your child space when they need it, sometimes they might not be ready to be cuddled, so sometimes being physically close and emotionally open is the best thing to do.

Use lots of eye contact.

Talk to your little one lots, think about the tone of your voice, especially before they can understand your words.

Your facial expression can say so much; if you look angry, upset, or distracted this can make your baby feel insecure.

Try to understand your child's unique ways of communicating.

Spend time giving your child your full attention, listen without interruption, play without distraction, connect fully with them (as much as you can, I appreciate it's not possible to always be 100% attentive, but your child knows the difference)

Respond to their need for emotional support, respond to their cries quickly.

Be consistent with your responsiveness; being left to cry one day then being responded to the next can be very unsettling.

Delight in who they are and what they do, be excited and happy with them, be interested and curious with them.

The Circle of Security International website has lots of resources about attachment and how to build it, I love how they explain 'everything I need to know about supporting security in 25 words or less':

"Always be: Bigger, stronger, wiser, and kind.
Whenever Possible: Follow my child's need.
Whenever necessary: Take charge."

But What if You Make Mistakes?

Nobody is the perfect parent. It's all well and good going through the list above but there are *always* going to be times that we miss the mark, and you can't beat yourself up over these.

Maybe we missed a cue they were trying to show us, maybe we're stressed from work and have a million and one things to do so are distracted and haven't the head space to play.

That's OK, often the repair of the momentarily broken bond is as important as being fully present and attentive all the time. It shows that we're only human. Having to live up to the idea of a 'perfect parent' is a big ask so it's OK if you get it wrong, as long as the repair is handled well.

Try to read what your child needs and make some time to reconnect. This can even strengthen the relationship and deepen trust. "I shouldn't have shouted at you just now, I'm sorry."

If you can keep in mind the basis of your child's fundamental need of attachment, it's going to help you to feel confident that you're doing the right thing by choosing responsive sleep coaching strategies, even when others may be telling you that you're not.

Speaking of sleep.... Let's get on with it!

CHAPTER 3

The Science Bit

This chapter will help you to understand sleep essentials, how biological sleep needs (don't) fit in with modern society and help you to understand what is realistic when considering your sleep goals.

Let's start with what is most parent's ideal sleep situation, what you see as sleep success if you like!

Many parents will tell me that whilst they fully expect some sleepless nights with their baby, the goal is for them to be sleeping through the night, and even better than that, to be sleeping through the night and also falling asleep without lots of parental support such as rocking or feeding to sleep.

We will talk about what is 'normal' as far as baby sleep is concerned, not to make you feel bad that it's so hard, but so you're able to set realistic expectations for what might be achievable for your child.

This is an important part of the process. There are so many opinions, old wives' tales, and cultural and societal expectations about sleep that it will be helpful for you to understand what the research says.

Sometimes this means you might see how your goals may be difficult to achieve straight away because your child may simply be too young, it is always better to have a goal that is achievable and within reach, rather than have one you 'think' is achievable but may not be, as this leads to a sense of anxiety and failure.

What is 'normal baby sleep'?

How have societal influences shaped your perception of how babies should sleep?

These are some of the things that my clients thought they should expect about baby sleep.

- "Babies sleep for up to 16 or more hours a day".
- "They should be able to sleep through by 6 months".
- "Children should be in bed by 7pm".
- "Sleeping through the night is sleeping from 7pm to 7am".
- "A 2-hour long lunchtime nap is important for brain development".
- "You're spoiling your baby if you cuddle them to sleep".
- "They don't need to feed in the night after 12 weeks (or XX weight)".
- "They need to learn to self-soothe".
- "Contact naps/pram naps/ car naps are not as good quality sleep as naps in the cot".
- "Babies should be in a routine that's the same every day".
- "They just need to link sleep cycles".

You may have already bought a range of sleep and feeding routines off the internet in those 3 am searches whilst you're trying to get your little one back to sleep again. But why don't they work? Why does your child just not conform to those timetables, if they 'need' to sleep 12 hours overnight and nap in the cot with little parental help, it should be so simple, right?

But what if you knew that those things aren't realistic or typical? That really, it's normal for babies to:

- Not sleep for long periods of time, day, or night, especially before age 1.
- Want to be supported to sleep by being held/rocked/fed etc.
- Often sleep better and for longer whilst being held.
- Wake easily when put down.

So, if your little one is doing any or all of the above, please be reassured that they are not broken and you're not doing something wrong., It just means they are sleeping in a biologically 'normal' way.

Equally if your child goes to bed at 7pm, sleeps for 12 hours with minimal or no waking and will happily fall asleep without help then that's also normal!

But of course, even though something is 'normal' it doesn't make it easy!

How much sleep do they need?

Lots of parents I work with are concerned that their child is always exhausted, and sleep deprived because they might be waking multiple times a night and only having 'short' naps...

We can be 'guilty' of projecting OUR tiredness onto our children "They must be shattered; they were up 3 times last night". But the truth is, infants are well equipped to deal with normal night waking, plus don't forget they nap, so they catch up then.

However, it is not that often that I come across a child who isn't somewhere within the 'average' range of sleep that research studies tell us they need (it's always the adults who are suffering though!).

Let us look at what 'average' looks like in two recent and large-scale studies.

Age	Average Sleep in 24 hours	Ranges from	Average # of Wakes
6-9 Months	12.6 hours	8.8 – 15.8 hours	1.7
12 Months	12.9 hours	10.1 – 15.8 hours	0.7
1-2 Years	12 hours	9.5 – 14 hours	1.1

Galland et al. 2012 Normal sleep patterns in infants and children: a systematic review of observational studies

Age	Average Day Sleep (Ranges from)	Average Night Sleep (Ranges from)	Average # Night Wakes (Ranges from)
3 months	5.3 hours (1 – 10.5 hours)	9.1 hours (2 – 12 hours)	2.2 (0 – 15)
6 months	3.7 hours (0.5 – 9 hours)	9.9 hours (2.5 – 12 hours)	2.5 (0 – 15)
8 months	3.4 hours (1 – 9 hours)	9.9 hours (6 – 12 hours)	2.4 (0 – 21.5)
12 months	2.1 hours (0.5 - 6 hours)	10.2 hours (3.5 – 12 hours)	1.8 (0 – 13.5)
18 months	2.1 hours (0.7 – 7.5 hours)	10.2 hours (5.5 – 12 hours)	1.1 (0 – 11)
24 months	1.9 hours (0 – 5 hours)	10 hours (6.8 – 12 hours)	0.9 (0 – 6)

Paavonen et al. 2020 Normal sleep development in infants: findings from two large birth cohorts. *Sleep Medicine*, 145-154

As you can see from both studies, it is common for children to still wake on average at least once a night up to 2 years old.

Another study found that that 85% of babies will still wake in the night until they are 18 months! (Hysing M, 2014)

What is also interesting to see is the in the second study, that babies tend not to sleep for 12 hours overnight.

The first study also found that babies slept somewhere around 12 or 13 hours in 24! If we are really to believe that our little ones will sleep for 12 hours overnight from 7pm-7am, then looking at this, they wouldn't need to nap during the day, but we all know that there is no way that they could make it through 12 hours during the day without a nap!

So once again I will repeat that your baby is not broken, and you are not doing anything wrong if your baby wakes through the night and doesn't sleep 7pm to 7am.

What it does perhaps indicate, is that you need to come up with a schedule that works for YOUR little one, one that is both realistic and achievable.

Why Do Babies Wake in the Night?

Have you ever wondered why babies wake in the night so much? Are they just manipulating us into giving them extra cuddles on demand or is it more than that?

- Babies are born with no Circadian Rhythm so don't know day from night in the first 10-12 weeks.

- After their sleep cycles mature, they are very easily disturbed at the end of each cycle until they drift between them less consciously like adults do.

- It is thought that frequent waking is protective against SIDS (sudden infant death syndrome)

- They have tiny tummies so need to feed frequently, especially in the early days.

- And, of course, those lovely periods of growth which result in sleep regressions which we will move onto shortly.

It's unfair of us to think of our children as being so simple that the only reason they wake in the night is due to hunger. There are so many other reasons why we wake in the night, the difference is how, we as adults, handle it. Let's think about why WE wake in the night.

Reason for Waking	How We Get Back to Sleep
Anxiety / Stress / Excitement	Distract / Rationalise
Need the bathroom	Go to the bathroom
Hot / Cold	Stick feet out / Adjust bedding
Thirst	Have a drink
Pain / Illness	Take medication / Distraction
Heard noise / Movement	Resolve / Distract
Light disturbance	Close curtains / move
We just don't know!	Any of the above

If we're feeling anxious, stressed, or excited it can make it hard to sleep. Maybe we have woken up after a nightmare, what do we do if this happens? We can distract our minds and rationalise with ourselves that it is all OK or we might speak to our partner for comfort.

Maybe we wake up needing to go to the bathroom, what do we do? Well of course we just go the bathroom!

If we are thirsty, we can get ourselves a drink.

If something hurts, we can go and take some pain relief or move position.

Maybe a noise has disturbed us, we can check it out and either stop the noise or rationalise with ourselves that we are safe.

But what do our babies do? They can't do any of the things we can do to take care of ourselves, so they must cry for help.

Please be reassured that your baby is not playing games with you or being manipulative when they cry in the night, they are simply demonstrating a need for care and support from us. By being responsive to their needs in the night you will not be making a rod for your own back but be supporting your child to build a secure attachment and feel safe and secure in their sleep space.

Regression / Progression?

What else is happening to our babies that affects their sleep? Brain development.

In the early years, our children's brains are going through a huge amount of change. As we've covered, they are born with around 30% of an adult's brain, and can manage a basic number of skills, but still solely rely on the parent to ensure they are able to survive the first weeks and months.

The human brain is amazing. Through experience and repetition, it makes more and more connections inside and learns and grows.

The first two years of life are critical to child development. So much so that the UK Government has formed the First 1001 Days Movement (from pregnancy to two years) to help support families in recognising and supporting the emotional wellbeing of infants.

Here are just some of the amazing milestones your baby's brain will meet over the first few years, not to mention going from being completely static to being able to roll, sit, crawl, and then walk!

Further than those huge and obvious physical developments, the brain is undergoing massive growth with communication and emotions.

By **3 months** – your baby is able to smile or cry to communicate.

Around **9-10 months** – memory is improving so separation anxiety and fear of strangers begin around this age.

By **18m – 2 years** – your toddler is learning about relationships between others and empathy. Language skills are booming daily.

At **3-4 years** – they are beginning to understand about sharing and taking turns, and other social skills are improving.

By **6-11 years** – logical thought comes in, and cause and effect start to make sense.

Do you know how old are we before our brain is fully emotionally mature? You may be surprised to know it is not until our late 20s!

Why Do Sleep Regressions Happen?

During these times of huge brain development, it's common that sleep will be affected, these periods are commonly known as sleep regressions. Whilst these periods are possibly a time when sleep may seem like it regresses, it is a sign that your little one is growing and developing and shouldn't be seen as a negative, as with anything with children, these tough times will pass!

Many sleep experts have now taken to calling these periods 'sleep PROgressions' instead.

But why do they happen?

Human brains are clever, they will prioritise they type of sleep needed for growth, repair, and development.

Deep Sleep – helps us to rest and recover and helps us to feel refreshed. It is the restorative sleep that allows for recovery and growth.

REM Sleep – this is active sleep where the brain is almost as busy as when we are awake, it is essential for functions like memory, learning and creativity. We are most easily woken in this sleep state.

It makes sense that if we need to do more REM sleep to be able to process what we have experienced and learned into memory, that babies will do more REM sleep during these times of growth and development. It also makes sense that as we are more easily disturbed in REM sleep, babies may start to wake more often too! Cue lots more waking.

What Can I Expect During Sleep Progressions?

It's not unusual for babies to also be grumpier during these times of development. Maybe its frustration or maybe they're more physically tired from learning their new skill, but it can mean that naps are a little more challenging. Your baby might need more comfort, or they just don't seem to know what they want!

At these times, your baby may need more help to fall asleep for naps and at bedtime, they may wake more frequently through the night, and they may start to fight or even refuse naps. This may go on for 2-4 weeks (sometimes more).

It can feel frustrating if things have been going well and you feel like you've been in a predictable routine that seems to work when suddenly everything is thrown in the air again.

When Do Sleep Progressions Happen?

As with anything relating to children, sleep regressions won't happen at the same time for all children, but in the first two years, you might notice that sleep goes a bit wonky around:

3-6 months (commonly known as the 4-month sleep regression).

8-10 months

12 months

14-18 months

I know what you're thinking – OMG Will I Ever Sleep Again? I know that it sounds horrendous that there are all these times in the first two years where sleep regressions might happen. I try and remind parents not to sit and count down the days to these periods as you might end up stressing unnecessarily about them, but if you notice that sleep has gone a little wonky, take a step back and look at your child. Have they learned a new skill? What has changed developmentally? If you can list things like rolling, grasping, sitting, crawling, walking, cruising, or babbling/talking, its highly likely that's what's up with sleep.

Do try to remember that not all babies go through all these blips, there are even some babies who just sleep well the whole time, but this is less common (hence why we call these babies unicorn babies). Of course, if you have a unicorn baby then you're not likely to be reading this book!

Can We Prevent Sleep Progressions Happening?

There's nothing you can do that will stop your baby's sleep regressions from happening, as they are a natural part of development, however following The Baby Sleep Blueprint my help reduce the impact or help you get back on track quicker.

How Can I Survive Sleep Progressions?

Often the best thing to do during your child's sleep regression is to focus less on trying to change what they are doing (there's already SO much going on in their brains) and try and focus on yourself and getting as much rest as you can.

Review the routine, is it time to tweak the timing/length of naps?

Ask for and take help if it is offered. Friends, family, whoever is a trusted contact. Take it, you are not superhuman, remember we are not supposed to be doing this alone!

Take it in shifts with your partner during the night, there's no point in you both being exhausted.

Rest when the baby sleeps. I know it's not always easy to sleep when the baby sleeps, but at least try to have a break (contact naps are a great excuse to take some time out, and you're helping your baby!)

If your baby has missed naps or the routine is all off, don't be afraid to bring bedtime earlier to compensate.

Expect there may be more night feeds and go with it. Babies need more calories during growth spurts and development leaps, so don't be surprised if your baby wants more food during the day. You may also find that your baby who may stopped feeding during the night needs one again.

Be consistent in your routine and settling approach, but don't worry if you feel like you're falling into old 'bad' habits. These times are tough, focus on getting through the here and now, you can always 'fix' things later. It is NEVER too late to get sleep on track, but it can be too early or not the 'ideal' time.

Ready to get a bit geeky?

I think it's important that you understand how sleep works, for you to be able to understand why we do what we do so that when you need to change something, you can do it instinctively. Unlike other sleep plans that just tell you how to do something, in this book you will also understand why.

Let's go through some common sleep phrases that I'll talk about throughout this book, but also give you a solid understanding of sleep biology.

Circadian Rhythm

The Circadian Rhythm is our internal body clock, it's what tells our body that we should be awake during the day and asleep at night.

Now you probably don't need me to tell you that our babies are born without their own circadian rhythm. It isn't actually fully established for around 12 weeks so until then your baby has no idea what is day and what is night and quite often, they can be wide awake for long periods during the night and asleep a lot during the day.

There are several external cues that drive the circadian rhythm.

The main cue is **light**, and it is the best way to help teach your baby the difference between day and night. Make daytime bright, as soon as you get up, open the curtains, and get as much natural light as possible (obviously don't leave your baby in direct sunlight though!). In winter you may need to switch all the lights on if it is still very dark outside. At night-time dim the lights in the evening or draw the curtains if it's Summertime.

Noise and social cues help regulate our circadian rhythm, so when you get up in the morning, be animated and use a daytime voice. Don't tiptoe around your baby during nap times either, just keep daytime noise at a normal level. You can do the reverse at night-time to help them recognise the difference!

Food – When fully established on solids, mealtimes are another way the body recognises the time of day. So, if your child is waking very early in the morning, it is a good idea to delay breakfast until a more 'normal' time, so it is in line with their natural body clock.

Temperature – Our body temperature drops in the evening, so avoid warm baths too close to bedtime (within an hour or two).

Think about when you travel to a different time zone; your circadian rhythm is out of sync with the location. How do we usually help ourselves to get over this jet lag? We eat meals at the new local time, and we are exposed to light, dark and noise. Did you realise that's how it all worked?

Sleep Hormones

Sleep and wakefulness are controlled by a number of hormones, the two main ones you need to know about are melatonin and cortisol.

Melatonin is the sleep hormone, and it is produced after around 2 hours in dim light. Our melatonin levels rise in the early evening and drop as the night goes on. Melatonin is naturally low when exposed to blue light. It's at its highest in the first part of the night and this is why the first few hours after your baby's bedtime are the most settled.

Cortisol is often referred to as the stress hormone. It drives our fight or flight response when under stress and can be damaging to brain development in excessive amounts (which is why I don't recommend leaving children to cry as a sleep strategy!). However, cortisol helps drive many other processes such as digestion and is also essential for us to stay wakeful and alert.

Cortisol begins to rise early in the morning, peaking a couple of hours after waking, and drops as the day goes on. If we don't go to sleep when our bodies need us to, we produce a shot of cortisol to keep us going. This is what we sometimes see as a 'second wind' in babies and children who have missed a nap or go to bed late. It's works much like when you have an espresso to tide you over when low on energy.

Sleep Pressure

Sleep pressure is the biological drive to sleep. It's controlled by another hormone, adenosine which is linked to digestion. Essentially when our food fuel is broken down and used up, adenosine triggers sleepiness in order to force us to rest and rebuild our energy reserves.

The interesting thing about sleep pressure (and this is why generic wake windows cannot be relied upon) is that it is not only controlled by how long we have been awake but also by how much exercise and stimulation we have experienced. We will cover the pros and cons of thinking about wake windows later in the book.

Think of sleep pressure as a pan of water on the hob, the gas being on is the effect of time, so steadily the pressure builds until the water boils. If your baby has a busy morning with lots of exercise or stimulation like a baby group or similar, then that gas is effectively being turned up and so the water will reach boiling point faster and they might need to nap earlier than usual.

Sleep Cycles

Babies are born with immature sleep cycles. They move between just two types of sleep – REM sleep and Deep Sleep.

They tend to spend most of their sleeping time in REM Sleep. This REM sleep is known as dreaming sleep and is essential for brain development. It is in this type of sleep that long and short-term memory is consolidated and brain synapses are made and pruned. During this sleep stage, they can twitch, groan, and sigh! Not what we expect when we think about the phrase sleeping like a baby!

During deep sleep, cells are growing and being repaired, the growth hormone is produced, and they are hard to rouse.

Between 3-6 months, our baby's sleep cycle matures into one more like an adult's. Although it is shorter, they now start to go through all the different types of sleep.

Here's a diagram to explain in more detail.

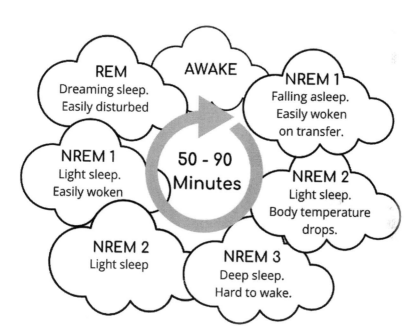

How can we recognise each sleep stage?

From being awake, they start in **NonREM 1** sleep. This is light sleep, during which they are easily disturbed by noise or by transferring them out of arms. You might recognise this type of sleep as they might twitch.

From there they move into a **deeper** sleep, also known as **slow-wave sleep**; in older children, this can be where night terrors, sleep walking and bedwetting can happen. You'll know this as their breathing will slow down and they'll be very still and hard to rouse.

Then they move into **REM sleep**, that state of dreaming sleep where they can be easily disturbed before going back into the next sleep cycle.

When this maturation first happens, it is commonly known as the 4-month sleep regression as they can often start waking more at night again (often every one or two hours). It can however happen any time between 3 & 6 months so don't sit there worrying and counting down the days to your baby turning 4 months, and it may not be as bad as you may have heard.

The length of infant sleep cycles starts at around 30-50 minutes between birth and preschool age where it increases to around 90 minutes rising gradually up to 90-120 minutes as an adult.

The type of sleep that happens in each cycle changes over the course of the night, starting with cycles that have more deep sleep in the first third of the night and towards the end of the night, they have more REM sleep. This is why we tend to see babies sleeping quite settled for the first part of the night and being more wakeful in the early hours of the morning.

During naps, babies may not always do a full sleep cycle; our brains are extremely clever and are fantastically capable of prioritising the type of sleep it needs, so don't worry if your little one catnaps and doesn't seem to get a lot of deep sleep. If they are generally happy and are meeting developmental milestones, it is probably all they need right now, and you can trust their brain to do what it needs.

CHAPTER 4

Temperament

As you will have realised by now, I do not have a one size fits all approach to sleep coaching. In my opinion, anyone who does is short-sighted and setting parents up to fail. Let's face it, if one thing worked for everyone then there wouldn't be any families who were struggling with sleep!

So, this chapter will cover what's arguably the most underestimated thing that impacts how you baby sleeps.

That thing is temperament. Our children are not robots, they are born with individual personality traits that are recognisable even in utero (Thomas et al. 1960).

Temperament is thought to come from both nature and nurture, with some traits recognisable even during pregnancy. The nature element is something we can't control or change, they are simply made that way! It's in their DNA!

However even the most challenging of temperament traits, supported and nurtured in the right way can become easier to parent and for the child to understand, regulate and thrive!

Mary Sheedy Kurcinka has written a fabulous book 'Raising Your Spirited Child' which is all about temperament and how to recognise the different traits and adapt your parenting. I highly recommend it as a brilliant read.

The list of traits Dr Kurcinka's book discusses are linked to those defined by Chess & Thomas:

Intensity – How strongly do they experience and show their emotions? Are they quick or slow to calm if dysregulated? Do they giggle quietly or laugh loudly?

Persistence – Do they find it hard to stop an activity? If they are playing and you need them to stop, do they fuss about it or will they easily move on? Do they react if a toy is taken off them? Are they calm or do they get very upset/frustrated? Are they a child who knows what they want, and won't rest until they get it?

Sensitivity – Do they seem to notice noises, temperature changes, textures, and tastes? Do they notice labels in clothes, seams in socks etc? Do they demand to be changed quickly after soiling their nappy?

Perceptiveness – Do they seem easily distracted? Maybe they seem to dwell on shadows, noises, patterns, or people? Does everything seem to catch their attention?

Adaptability – Do they seem to struggle with change? Different routines or environments? Is changing their nappy a challenge?

Regularity – Are they quite regular about eating and sleeping times (like when they wake in the morning), how much sleep they need, or when they need to go to the toilet?

Energy – Are they always on the go, or are they calm and quiet? Do they seem to have endless energy no matter how little sleep they've had?

First Reaction – Are they slow to warm up to somewhere or someone new, or do they get stuck right in?

Mood – Are they generally happy or more serious?

If you score your child 1-5 for each trait, you can get a good idea overall whether your child is a higher need or as Dr Kurcinka describes 'spirited', child.

It makes sense that the more mellow and 'easy-going' children are often those who sleep better, have more ability to 'self soothe', and adapt to changes to routines. All of which makes the parenting journey feel that little bit 'easier'.

Children who are on the extreme end of the scale can be seen as difficult, needy, and 'high maintenance'. If you are a parent of one of these children, it can feel like you're not doing a good job because these kids almost always need more, no matter what you've done for them (poor parental self-efficacy) (Cutrona and Troutman, 1986) it's common that you'll have negative feelings about these traits, and it can be challenging, taking a lot of energy, time, and patience.

What's also interesting is that research also shows that if you have poor parental self-efficacy, you can view your child's temperament negatively.

Do You Recognise These Traits?

You may not instantly recognise these personality traits in your own child, but these are some of the common phrases I hear from parents who have 'spirited' children. Do you ever hear or say these things about your child?

"Oh, I always know exactly what they're feeling, they don't need to tell me!" (Intense)

"They never stop, they're on the go all the time, I can't keep up!" (Active)

"They go from nought to sixty if I do not get to them quickly" (Reactive)

"They can be completely asleep in my arms then as soon as I put them down, they wake, and I have to start all over again" (Sensitive)

"They have major FOMO (Fear of missing out)" (Alert)

"They don't ever self-soothe" (Intense)

"I just know they wouldn't stop crying even if I tried the cry it out, or controlled crying methods" (Persistence)

"They don't handle it well if we change up the bedtime routine, nappy changes are difficult" (Not Adaptable)

"They just cling on to me when we go to a new play group, it takes ages for them to warm up" (First reaction)

"They just do not sleep.... ever..." (all of the above!)

How this affects sleep

The following table lists the more challenging temperament traits and how they impact sleep, reframes them in a positive light and gives you some ideas of how to handle them day to day.

Traits	Positives	Impact on Sleep	Parenting Strategies
Intense or **Reactive** children experience emotions acutely. 0-60 in 10 seconds! Not a 'self-soother'	Experience life intensely, enthusiastic, driven, energetic; great to motivate others as a leader!	May cry lots, even with the gentlest of strategies. Resists change strongly, even seemingly small changes.	Focus on regulation, avoid over-stimulation. Watch for dysregulation cues (see Zones Of Arousal)

The Better Sleep Blueprint

Traits	Positives	Impact on Sleep	Parenting Strategies
Perceptive or **Alert** children don't miss a thing. Serious FOMO. Spot when routines are different, this distracts them from settling. Can't understand when you change rules.	These kids take in more information. Recognise patterns and routines. They can be really engaged.	Notices small inconsistencies in routine / sleep space. Hard to read sleep cues. Often don't nap well. Resists change.	Keep routines and sleep environment the same. Read the same book last each night or singing the same songs over and over. Demand stimulation but can easily go over the edge.
Persistent kids never give up. They know what they want. Demand more all the time! Whine and cry for what they want.	Persistence is a good thing! A 'can-do' attitude can help them to go far in life.	May take longer to change routines / sleep associations. They resist change, so be prepared to be consistent and committed!	Encourage them to do things for themselves. Hold boundaries for the things that matter. Say yes as much as you can to give them some control.

41

The Better Sleep Blueprint

Traits	Positives	Impact on Sleep	Parenting Strategies
Sensitive children need careful support. Light sleeper. Sensitive to smells, textures, temperatures, tiredness. Get upset easily when a caregiver is upset/stressed/angry	Feel all the feels. Can be sensitive to people's feelings, empathetic. Cautious, careful, and selective are positive traits to have!	Easily over stimulated Resists change.	Watch for over-stimulation. E.g., does a bath calm them or stimulate? Regulate your own emotions around them. Consider the sensory environment – sounds, light, smells, textures, and touch.
Irregular temperament kids have no obvious routines, Are unpredictable with hunger and sleep.	Become society's shift workers. Paramedics, police etc! Are flexible, cope well without structure.	Will not respond to set sleep schedules, no matter how hard you try. They wake, nap, go to sleep at different times each day.	Trust their cues over the clock. Accept the unpredictable, let go of your own need for control or routines.

Every day is different to the next		They don't poo at regular times!	Get up at the same time each day to try to encourage some predictability.

According to Macall Gordon M.A. from Little Livewires, if you have a child with one or more of the above personality traits, research showed that:

- Parents who had a difficult labour or birth were slightly more likely to have to have a child they describe as 'alert'.
- Your child was more likely to have had reflux/colic/food intolerance.
- You have tried sleep training and it did not work or it was way worse than it should be.

If you have a child who is on the more extreme side of the scale for any of the temperament traits, you might find parts of your parenting journey more challenging. You might even feel like it is your fault that they do not sleep or that what you are trying isn't working.

Please recognise that these traits do have positives too, and they are not something you can control but by understanding your child's personality and temperament, you can choose a strategy that aligns more with their needs, as well as beginning to understand why they are behaving or reacting the way they are.

How to Manage These Traits During Sleep Coaching

Try to look at these personality traits from the positive side if you can. None of them are bad or wrong, after all, we are all unique!

Be prepared for a lot of protesting during the coaching process.

You may need to intervene quickly if your child is getting dysregulated.

They react strongly to change so even what feels like a baby step may be huge for them.

They may need more sleep support for longer than an 'easy-going' child.

They can be easily overstimulated as they have such active brains.

They love and crave patterns and routines, so if they can detect one, they will often settle in well. You may need to be rigidly consistent in your routine.

Stick at it – active and alert children often take a while to 'get it'. It might feel like you're not getting anywhere but one day it will just click.

Push through push back – you are there to support and calm your child through the change. Have a look at the chapter on the 'extinction burst' and emotion coaching.

Regulation

Babies and children are unable to calm themselves down from a state of arousal because their brains are just not wired that way yet.

Your child relies on you for support with this, and if you have a 'spirited' child your regulation skills are most likely going to be needed a whole lot more!

Dr Kurcinka talks about the zones of arousal in her book. The idea is based around a traffic light system of cues that children demonstrate when they are calm through to overwhelmed dysregulation.

In the green zone, they are happy and relaxed, all is well with the world.

In the yellow zone, they may be starting to feel dysregulated. At this stage, you might be able to bring them back down to 'green' by taking a break, having a change of scenery, a snack, drink, or nap.

In the red zone, they are completely overloaded and need serious help and time to calm down.

Ideally you will get to know your own child's green, yellow and red cues and try to keep them in the green zone as much as possible.

The GREEN Zone All Is Well	The YELLOW Zone I'm Struggling	The RED Zone I Need Major Help
Makes eye contact	Looks away	Cries
Actively plays	Loses interest	Throws themselves back
Calm	Fusses a bit	Whines and screams
Happy	Seeks contact	Clenched fists
Has calm body movements	Jerky body movements	Stiff body
Giggles	Frowns	Pulls up knees
Breathes quietly and slowly	Faster breaths, sighs	Shouts, screams or cries
Alert and looks around	Blinking a lot more	Grimacing
Interacts with others	Pushes things or people away	Throws things
Smiles	Hiding under blanket	Screaming

Explores	Gets irritable, comes for comfort	Seek comfort but pushes you away
Calmly looks around	Hiccups	Frantically looking around

How can you bring your child down from a state of dysregulation?

- Touch (cuddles, holds & massage).
- Sucking (offer a finger, or dummy).
- Warmth.
- Movement / rocking.
- Low sound, think white noise or humming.
- Show them something new, a new toy, a book, look out of the window.
- Play some music for them, or sing. There are lots of studies which have found that music positively affects stress behaviours (Caine, 1991), and the sound of the mothers' voice has positive therapeutic effects (Standley and Moore, 1995).
- Get outside in nature or to a parent group for moral support.

If you're finding it hard to regulate your own emotional state whilst your child is dysregulated, head over to chapter 15 for some tips.

CHAPTER 5

Unsettled Babies

W e've established that baby sleep is hard but how do we know whether it's 'normal-hard' or there's something more going on? It is reasonably common that what presents as a sleep problem is rooted in another issue. Here we will explore some of the common medical reasons that impact baby sleep.

Conditions like reflux, eczema, mouth breathing, or allergies, as well as feeding issues contributing to faltering growth, can all be linked with sleep problems. With that in mind, it is important to have any medical or feeding problems resolved before working hard trying to change sleep. So please check in with your GP, Infant Feeding Team, or Health Visitor to discuss whether it's appropriate to start sleep coaching.

Without resolving any medical issues that may be affecting sleep, the efficacy of any sleep coaching strategies will be reduced.

Some things to consider are mouth breathing, allergies, reflux, tongue tie, iron deficiency and tension.

Mouth breathing

Mouth breathing or snoring that happens even when your little one doesn't have a cold, could indicate sleep apnoea/sleep disordered breathing, and should be investigated further by GP/ENT.

As parents, we often spend a lot of time thinking and watching our children sleep. It's fair to say that sometimes the position they settle in or the way they move around can be amusing (I never could understand how my son would sleep on his front with his bum in the air!) or cute (those little snores).

However, could some of these things be a sign of something more?

Sleep Apnoea is a condition which affects between one and five percent of children, causing their breathing to stop and start during sleep. It is more common in children with sickle cell disease and Down Syndrome.

The long-term health risk comes from chronic sleep deprivation as the brain constantly wakes the child to breathe. Chronic sleep deprivation affects behaviour, cognitive ability, anxiety and depression, diabetes, obesity, and many other health problems.

How do you know whether your child has sleep apnoea?

Snoring

Snoring is normal, right? Cute when my kid or puppy does it, not so cute when my husband does it!

But is snoring normal in kids?

Well, no it isn't, actually, and it could be a sign that there is something wrong. So, if your little one is a regular snorer or mouth breather (and not just when they have a cold a couple of times year) then read on.

Snoring is where air flows past the relaxed tissues in the throat, causing them to vibrate and produce that (annoying when you're trying to sleep) sound.

It's fair to say that if your child is snoring it's quite possible that they are not getting good quality sleep. This can affect their mood, behaviour, and cognitive ability. Long term, this can affect their education milestones.

Often, snoring can be related to chronic allergy where the nose and throat are inflamed or blocked, or it could be obstructive sleep apnoea.

Waking Up Upset

Whilst it is quite normal for children to cry in the night and need parental support, some children with sleep apnoea wake in a fright. It makes sense, doesn't it? You may even hear them gasp for air as they wake up.

This may also happen during the daytime as sleep apnoea isn't only a night-time occurrence.

Moves Around a Lot

Children who move around a lot in bed could be doing so because they are trying to find the best position for a clear airway. If your child seems to sleep in an uncomfortable-looking position with their neck extended backward, they could be struggling with sleep apnoea.

Challenging Behaviour

If your child seems 'hyperactive', irritable, or easily upset, it could be that they are sleep deprived as a result of being disturbed in the night through sleep apnoea.

Slow Eater

Large tonsils, which can cause sleep apnoea can make it difficult for children to eat as it's hard to swallow and breathe at the same time. Therefore, some children with apnoea will appear to be fussy or slow eaters during the day.

Recurrent Colds

Children with large tonsils/adenoids have a reduced capacity for breathing. If they catch a cold or virus is causes inflammation and further reduces the airway. If your child seems to always pick up colds, it's worth having the GP check out their throat.

What to do

Some of these symptoms are common things for children to experience, but if you recognise a couple of them in your own little one, it is worth getting them checked out by your GP/ENT Specialist.

You may be referred for a sleep study which measures breathing and heart rate while they sleep.

Sleep apnoea may be treated by removing tonsils/adenoids, nasal spray, mouth guards or other treatments.

Lots more information can be found at https://www.blf.org.uk/support-for-you/osa-in-children

Allergies

Especially in the early days, one of the only ways our babies can communicate with us is by crying.

Sometimes the reason babies and children are unsettled and unhappy is due to digestive discomfort, which could be due to an allergy. If your child has any of the symptoms described below, it might be worth reviewing their diet (and yours if breastfeeding exclusively) as without resolving the root cause, you may not be able to make improvements.

Tummy Discomfort

Most allergy symptoms are gut-related, symptoms like bloating, mucous in the stools, wind, reflux, colic, diarrhoea, and constipation. These symptoms often mean babies will vomit, squirm, and arch their backs, or even refuse feeds.

Skin Irritation

Allergies can cause dry flaky skin which can be itchy and sore. In some babies, it may cause long term cradle cap or make them sweat a lot. They may get hives or even dark circles under their eyes.

Respiratory Issues

If your child has frequent coughs, wheezing, asthma, a constant runny nose all the time, or even recurring ear infections, croup, and bronchitis it could be related to allergies.

The most common allergy in the UK is to cow's milk protein (CMPA) and soy, both of which are contained in formula milk, but of course babies could be allergic to dust, pollen, detergents, or pets too.

What Can You Do?

If your child has any of the symptoms in the points above, try the following tips.

Consider changing your washing powders/liquids/cleaning products.

Speak to your GP for support and try keeping a food diary and track the symptoms to see if you can see a link to a food type. If there's an obvious link, you could try eliminating that food type. If there's no obvious link, you could try cutting out dairy from your diet. If you are breastfeeding, then you will need to review your diet as well as your baby's. If your baby is on formula or you combination feed, you should see your GP as you may need a prescription formula.

Unfortunately, some of the prescription formula smell and tase different. If your baby refuses it, you can try to start by mixing with regular formula then reducing the ratio until it is just the new formula or try dream feeds where you pick them up and feed them whilst they are half asleep.

If your baby has irritated skin, regular application of emollient creams is essential. Itching is worse at night-time as cortisol which tames inflammation drops, so you might find that your child's skin seems to irritate them more in the evening.

The National Eczema Society suggests applying the creams at every nappy change and after bathing, applying them in a smooth, downward motion.

Reflux

Reflux is where a baby is sick after feeds. For some babies this is very painful and means that they are extremely uncomfortable when lying down. This has obvious implications for sleep!

In most cases reflux will improve as your baby grows and doesn't always need treatment, however if it is causing extreme discomfort then it's worth chatting to your GP.

Symptoms of reflux

- Baby is sick after feeds.
- Unsettled feeds
- Gulping or swallowing after burps
- Slow weight gain/ weight loss
- Crying and hard to settle especially when lying down.

Some babies have these symptoms but aren't sick which is called silent reflux.

Ideally if breastfeeding you would ask for some support in optimising your baby's latch and feeding position. If you bottle feed your baby, do it with them sitting upright and practice paced feeding where you hold the bottle horizontally and allow your baby to control the flow of the milk, taking plenty of pauses. Consider smaller, more frequent feeds as large feeds may cause the reflux to worsen.

To help your baby you should keep them upright for 30 minutes after feeds.

Reflux can be linked to allergies, so it could also be worth following the tips in the allergy section above. If you can resolve the cause, the reflux will reduce.

Tongue Tie

Babies with a tongue tie can have sleep problems for a couple of reasons. They may not be feeding effectively which may cause wind or digestive issues or growth problems, but a tongue tie may also link to airway obstruction and/or incorrect tongue position.

The tongue should rest behind the top teeth at the roof of the mouth when awake and asleep. When the tongue is in this position, breathing is through the nose, and we swallow correctly, and the vagus nerve is being stimulated.

The vagus nerve is the main nerve that runs from the brain to part of the colon, it sends information from the gut to the brain (hence the phrase 'gut feeling'), and it is part of the parasympathetic nervous system which controls our 'rest and digest' functions. If this nerve is not properly stimulated, it can mean we have a heightened stress response, and find it hard to come back to a state of rest after a stressful event.

This can mean that babies may need to feed more (or suck more) to bridge that gap and stimulate their palate for self-regulation. Ever wondered why kids suck their thumb for comfort? Well, the position of the thumb hit's just that spot.

So, children whose tongue tie either hasn't been revised, or has been revised but the function of the tongue still isn't correct (oral myofascial dysfunction) will probably seem unsettled. You often see babies with this problem waking very frequently, even hourly. An experienced tongue tie practitioner should be able to review this and assist with some oral exercises.

Tension / Torticollis / Plagiocephaly

Some babies carry tension in their bodies. This may come from the birth or preferring being fed in certain positions, or plagiocephaly (a flattening of the head) due to spending a lot of time on their backs. By the way this is not a reason to stop putting babies on their backs to sleep as safe sleep guidelines recommend, so make plenty of time for tummy time during the day.

If you find your baby lies in odd positions (like a banana), has a strong preference for their head being on one side, you could seek the advice of your GP or a cranial osteopath for additional support and or tension release.

Low Iron / Ferritin

Ferritin is a protein that stores iron in your blood. Having low ferritin is different to having low iron, you can have enough iron but with low ferritin, the body is not able to store, absorb and use it.

Babies are at risk as they grow so quickly (iron is needed for growth) and they don't generally have an iron rich diet. They can also have low ferritin if the mother was anaemic in pregnancy, they had early cord clamping, or drink cow's milk before 12 months (amongst some other reasons).

Low ferritin impacts the structure of the sleep cycles (Peirano et al, 2010), impacting the quality of sleep but also links to a childhood version of Restless Legs Syndrome (Periodic Limb Movement Disorder) where the child's legs may twitch, and they can't settle or get comfortable.

Look for the following symptoms,

- Babies who are awake for hours in the night and nothing seems to settle them.
- They may moan or seem uncomfortable.
- Crave extreme full body contact, constant feeding/suckling.
- Have a long Sleep Onset Latency (how long it takes to fall asleep – it should be around 15 mins)
- Children with allergies may be more susceptible to low iron if their gut is inflamed (as this can slow iron absorption).
- A family history of restless leg syndrome (RLS) or low iron in pregnancy

Speak to your GP for support, although unfortunately in the UK GPs are not usually keen to test iron levels.

If you think low iron could be an issue, you could ask the pharmacist if there are any iron supplements suitable for your baby.

Additionally look to supplement the diet with iron rich foods, eaten alongside oranges which can help iron absorption. Taking a vitamin B12 and folic acid supplement could also help, so seek advice from a chemist.

CHAPTER 6

Safe Sleep

No sleep coaching strategy is worth ignoring the safe sleep guidelines for, no matter how tired you are, in fact that's when it's even more important. It is essential that you follow these, wherever and whenever your little one goes to sleep.

- They should sleep in a clear cot (no bumpers/soft toys/loose blankets)
- The mattress should be firm, flat, and waterproof and fit tightly to the bed frame, leaving no gaps.
- You should always put them on their back to sleep. Don't worry when they start rolling – you don't have to stay awake all night to turn them back over, but you should still put them on their backs to sleep.
- If you choose to co-sleep, follow the safe guidelines.
- They should sleep in the same room as you for at least the first 6 months.
- Avoid your baby getting too hot by keeping the room between 16 and 20 degrees, dressing them appropriately and keeping baby's head uncovered.
- Protect them from smoke (and second hand smoke) both during pregnancy and afterwards.
- Breastfeeding significantly helps to protect infants from death including deaths from SIDS/SUDI and from secondary

disease and/or congenital conditions (University of Notre Dame)

- Babies should never sleep on sofas or couches with or without adults.

Co-Sleeping

Thankfully here in the UK the advice about co-sleeping is moving towards informed choice. It has been recognised that the messaging that discourages parents from ever bedsharing with their babies may have been unknowingly leading parents to follow unsafe sleep practices, therefore putting their babies at risk.

One common concern about co-sleeping is fear of hurting the baby by rolling onto them, however Dr James McKenna (an American anthropologist who studies infant/mother sleep behaviour) notes that for cultures where co-sleeping is the norm, SIDS rates are low. So, it's important to note that co-sleeping itself, in the optimal circumstances is not inherently dangerous.

The research shows that SIDS risk increases with co-sleeping when:

- The parent or partner smokes.
- The parents have consumed alcohol or drugs (this includes prescription drugs that cause drowsiness).
- The baby was of low birth weight or premature.

Some additional things Dr McKenna says to consider when bed sharing.

- Bottle-fed babies should always sleep alongside the mother *on a separate surface* rather than in the same bed.
- Bedsharing should be a family decision and both parents involved should consider themselves primary caregivers,

both equally responsible for the baby and comfortable with the decision.

- Do not place the baby in bed with a parent who is already asleep.
- No siblings sharing the same bed before the baby is 1 year old.
- Long hair should be tied up to prevent strangulation.
- A co-sleeper bed attached separately should be used if the parent is extremely obese or would otherwise find it hard to feel how close the baby is to them.

His final point, and one that I will quote directly as I can't say it any better myself…, *"it may be important to consider or reflect on whether you would think that you suffocated your baby if, under the most unlikely scenario, your baby died from SIDS while in your bed. Just as babies can die from SIDS in a risk-free solitary sleep environment, it remains possible for a baby to die in a risk-free co-sleeping/bedsharing environment. Just make sure, as much as this is possible, that you would not assume that if the baby died, that either you or your spouse would think that bed-sharing contributed to the death, or that one of your really suffocated (by accident) the infant. While this is an unpleasant and uncomfortable topic, it is one that is worth thinking about before you make the choice to co-sleep/bedshare with your infant."*

More information on safe sleep can be found at

- https://www.lullabytrust.org.uk/
- https://www.basisonline.org.uk/

CHAPTER 7

The DNA Method

Now if you're happy that you understand the biology of sleep, safe sleep and you have ruled out any major reasons for unsettledness, you're ready to get going! If you have skipped ahead to this section as you're desperate to read the fix, I implore you to go back and read the first few chapters, it might save you some time and frustration in the long run.

We have already learned that there are many variables when it comes to baby sleep, so where on earth do you start when it comes to trying to make improvements?

This is why I am sharing with you my step by step **'DNA Method'**.

This is the method I use with all my 1:1 sleep coaching clients, and whilst the details within each step are unique to every family, the overall process is the same.

You might be surprised to know that I rarely tackle night sleep problems first. Problems at night-time are often affected by lots of other things; if we work on those first it can often make the night times improve without you needing to do anything else, and if not, it will at the very least help making changes in the evening easier.

How Does It Work?

The DNA Method is simply the order we tackle things.

 **is for Daytime.**

Start by reviewing what's happening during the day. Often there are many ways we can tweak what we do during the daytime that can have a positive impact on what happens at night-time.

- Have a look at the day sleep, compare your diary to the averages. Are they getting too much sleep or not enough? Consider their mood – even if they are on the lower end, if they are happy and meeting developmental milestones, that might be OK for them.
- Are the naps timed well and spread reasonably evenly across the day?
- Pay attention especially to the gap between the last nap and bedtime; overtiredness and dysregulation at bedtime can cause night-time issues.
- Work on great daytime sleep hygiene.
- Playtime, stimulation, and connection time are key during the day. Often in our modern lives, our little ones don't get enough exercise which can mean they are filled with energy in the evenings. Enjoying the connection that comes from spending quality time together during the day will also fill up their love tank, essential for a more compliant bedtime!

NOTE: you are not trying to change things like where your baby sleeps at this first stage. This part is all about making sure your timings and activities are working well so your baby is ready for sleep in the evening. If part of your goal is to transition your baby to their cot or own room, that will come later. Get the timings working well first so that these big changes are easier.

N is for Night-Time.

Whilst working on the daytime, you can also review what's going on at night-time.

What happens at the end of the day can also have a big impact on bedtime and overnight. You can be getting your little one ready to sleep a couple of hours before bedtime!

- Avoid overtiredness by understanding what time they need to be asleep by. This can be a bit of trial and error but learning your child's unique tired signs and tolerance for being awake is helpful.
- Plan when to start your evening flow of activities by working backward from the time they need to be asleep.
- Create a calm, nurturing, and consistent bedtime routine. Include activities that you both enjoy and that you can do in the same order every night.

NOTE: You can work on D elements and N elements of the process at the same time.

is for Sleep Associations

Finally, when you have covered the foundations above, you can look at working on sleep associations. Sleep Associations are the things your little one needs to help them to go to sleep, common ones are rocking, feeding, being bounced, pushed in the pram, or walked in a sling.

These associations are not bad habits as often we are led to believe, after all it's our job as parents to support our children to fall asleep, but one of the most common sleep goals for parents is for their children to be able to fall asleep without lots of parental intervention like rocking or feeding to sleep.

I'm all for having an easy life so if feeding or rocking your baby to sleep works and you are happy to do it, please don't let anyone tell you that you shouldn't. The challenge comes when you get to the point when you're done, you might feel touched out from breast/chest feeding, or it might feel hard to be the only one doing all the naps, bedtime, and night wakes, or simply that it becomes too physically demanding to rock your 1-year-old to sleep each night.

This book gives you not just one method to try, but a range of my favourite settling strategies so you can choose the one that's right for you and your child. None of them involve ever closing your door and ignoring your crying child.

CHAPTER 8

D is for Daytimes

Sleep Hygiene is the process of creating healthy, positive sleep habits; look after this and you will often see improvements without needing to do anything else. You're going to hear all the best daytime sleep hygiene tips in this next chapter.

Believe it or not, a good night's sleep starts in the daytime so reviewing and optimising sleep hygiene is always the first thing I work on with 1-2-1 coaching clients.

Consistent Wake Up Time

Wake up at a similar time every day (even weekends!!). Those weekend lie-ins can mess up the circadian rhythm so try to stick to one time, ideally no later than 7.30 am (give or take half an hour), especially if you'd like an evening – remember the later they wake in the morning, the later they'll go to bed in the evening.

Yes, this will sometimes mean waking your little one up! Obviously if things are going well with sleep, then you don't need to be doing this every day but whilst you are trying to establish a routine, this should help.

It may sound tough, especially when your nights are disrupted, but waking your little one **no later than 7.30 am** every day not only helps to kick start the Circadian Rhythm, but rising at the same time every day will help to give you some more predictability to your nap routine.

Daylight

Expose them to lots of broad-spectrum daylight. Remember that light is the main driver of the circadian rhythm.

Use it to your advantage by getting your little one exposed to daylight by opening all the curtains, or switching the lights on as soon as you can after they wake for the day and provide as much (safe) exposure as possible during their day. This is the biggest cue to the body that it is daytime and time to be awake. We will do the opposite at night.

Exercise

Give them plenty of opportunity for exercise and play – children need plenty of age-appropriate exercise, and they need to be physically as well as mentally stimulated. Playing with your little one also helps to fill up their love tank, we will talk about this in more detail in the bedtime routine chapter.

Up to the age of 1 – babies need around 30 mins of tummy time, (think of it more like 'off their back' time if they don't enjoy being placed on their tummies) with plenty of encouragement to sit, roll, reach, stand (if they want to) for short periods. Remember not to force them to do this before they are ready though, children learn in sequences, and pushing them to do things before they are ready can mean they miss important stages out which can have an impact later.

You can encourage movement and play by making obstacle courses for mobile babies by using cushions from the sofa and encouraging them to crawl over them.

At 1-2 years they should have around 3 hours of physical activity per day

Big body play (roughhousing) and games like tickle time are a great way of expelling excess energy before bedtime and help to build connection after a day apart.

Don't feel like you need to be a children's entertainer the whole time, it's also good for children to have time to safely explore their environment independently, it's all about balance.

Consistent Mealtimes

Once your child is fully established on solids, try to keep meals at regular times. Food is another cue for the circadian rhythm, so keep things consistent and offer plenty of healthy snacks in between meals and lots of water, milk, or diluted squash to drink.

However, if you baby is still primarily on milk, feeding responsively rather than on a feeding schedule is best for baby.

Evenly spaced naps

Spread naps evenly across the day if they're having more than one. Don't worry though, we will go into lots more detail about naps now as I KNOW how much naps stress parents out. So read on for all you need to know about naps.

CHAPTER 9

Naps

N aps are a big source of stress for many parents, whether it's that your little one won't be put down in the cot without waking after 30 minutes, or that it feels like you spend more time trying to get them to nap than the time they spend napping!

Often, we find the fact that not all babies seem to have a predictable nap routine very difficult to cope with.

I'm dedicating a whole chapter to naps; why do babies need to nap and how can you start to find a routine that suits your baby?

Are Naps Different to Night Sleep?

Yes, day sleep is different to night-time sleep. Firstly, the need to nap is driven by sleep pressure. Remember that sleep pressure is that biological urge to sleep and it is controlled by a different hormone, adenosine rather than melatonin. Adenosine production does not require dim light like melatonin does. Adenosine is essentially the hormone that tells our body that we need to sleep to rebuild our energy reserves, it builds whist we are awake and falls when we sleep.

The purpose of day sleep is to manage our little one's sleep pressure until bedtime. Getting the timing of naps and the amount of sleep in the day working well can help to improve sleep at night-time.

What many parents find frustrating about naps is that they are often not as long as we would like them to be; after all what can we realistically achieve in 30 minutes (especially when we can't put them down for the first 10 minutes of that!)?!

Many sleep plans revolve around a blissful 2 hour-long lunchtime nap, but this isn't always realistic for younger babies, and trying to aim for that will just result in you being stressed out every day. I tend to find the naps get longer when your child is only doing 1 (sometimes 2) a day.

> *"The brain is exceptionally good at working out what type of sleep it needs and how much sleep it needs.*
> *Babies' sleep cycles gradually get longer as they get older, and they start to have less active sleep when they are ready for that.*
> *You can't do anything to lengthen your baby's sleep cycle, and nor would you want to".*
> Lyndsey Hookway

Nap Myths and Truths

Let's debunk some of the myths you may have heard about naps firstly to reassure you, but also to give you a starting point for understanding what 'might' be going wrong if your little one's naps are driving you mad!

NAP MYTHS

- **Contact/Motion naps aren't good quality sleep.** You may have heard that if your baby naps in the car/pram/sling or anywhere else apart from their cot, that this type of sleep isn't restorative. It simply isn't true so feel free to use cuddles or movement for as long as you want to, to get your little one to nap.

- **Your baby should have a 2-hour nap at lunchtime for brain development.** Many online sleep guides revolve around this 2-hour nap from very early on. The difficulty here is that it is extremely common for many younger babies to catnap – i.e., to do short (30/40 minute) naps a few times during the day. It's often not until they are regularly doing 3 or even 2 naps a day that they tend to naturally extend past that. It's not doing your little one any harm at all to catnap. If they seem happy in their mood, short naps are probably perfectly OK for them!

- **Sleep Breeds Sleep.** Well, there is some truth in the fact that managing sleep pressure during the day with well-spaced naps might mean that the night goes a little smoother. BUT we all have an overall amount of sleep that we need in 24 hours so if your little one is sleeping for too long in the day, they simply won't need to sleep for as long at night.

- **Never wake a sleeping baby.** Re-iterating the point above, if your little one's naps aren't well-timed, or they are sleeping for too long then it's fine to wake them, and life (school runs, baby classes etc.) gets in the way sometimes, right?

- **Short Naps aren't restorative.** As mentioned in the previous lesson, our brains are very good at prioritising the type of sleep we need. So, if your baby is a cat-napper but is generally a happy little bunny, those catnaps are just fine.

- **You should avoid the 'danger nap'.** A danger nap is a nap taken 'late' in the afternoon which affects the child's usual bedtime, typically making it later than normal. Parents often worry that little ones sleeping later than 4/5pm is going to cause all sorts of problems. This means that some parents will try to prevent little ones from falling asleep and keep them awake until bedtime.

Firstly, let me clarify that in older children, I have no problem with parents worrying about keeping a consistent and reasonably timed bedtime when a 'late' nap means that bedtime will end up being 10 or 11pm. After all this often means they will be tired the next day and this isn't ideal when there's school or other important plans... and of course, they don't get to nap to catch up the next day.

Where I do ask parents to reconsider the concept of the danger nap is when you have a younger baby (between 3 and 18 months), when wake windows are typically 2-4 hours long. In this case, I usually just recommend you let them have a quick nap (maybe a power nap) if they need it then just do a slightly later bedtime.

NAP TRUTHS

- **A long nap in the morning can cause sleep problems.** If your little one takes their longest nap of the day in the morning, it means they must get through the rest of the day until bedtime with only a short nap. This can sometimes cause overtiredness or dysregulation at bedtime.

- **A long morning nap or short gap between waking and nap 1 can reinforce early waking.** For early risers (i.e., babies who wake before 6am) leaving only a short gap between waking and nap 1 can mean they continue with the early wake because they know they can catch up! So, if your little one regularly wakes early in the morning, try to keep them up for their 'usual' wake window, certainly longer than 90 minutes if they can make it.

- **A late nap or too long a nap at the end of the day can cause bedtime problems.** Most parents understand the 'danger nap' where if your little one sleeps too late in the day, it means that they won't be ready for bed. It makes sense, right? It takes off that sleep pressure, which means a later bedtime will usually be needed! However, I don't usually recommend missing an afternoon nap just to avoid a later bedtime, I believe it's much better to avoid overtiredness and dysregulation at bedtime and have a power nap if needed.

- **Naps should be spread evenly across the day to prevent sleep pressure from building too much by bedtime.** Getting to understand your little one's tolerance for how long they can be awake can be a game-changer. Review the tables in the previous section for averages, but really getting to know what works for your little person is important.

Spotting the Signs

Now you know that naps are all about managing sleep pressure and getting to grips with how long YOUR little one can tolerate being awake for.

If your little one takes short naps and wakes up grumpy, or it is a real battle to get them to nap, it's possible that the timing is off. Remember nobody can force someone else to fall asleep if they're not ready to and it really hard to keep someone awake when they need to go to sleep.

So, if you're spending 30 minutes or more trying to get your little one to nap then they're just not ready.

Ask yourself whether the signs you thought were tiredness may have been a need for a change of scenery or hunger?

Nap battles might also happen if your child is awake for too long which means they are harder to settle due to that shot of cortisol their body has produced to keep them awake. Or at the other end of the spectrum, you might be trying to put them down too early which means they are just not ready to sleep and therefore it's taking a lot of time and effort.

A general rule of thumb is that if it is taking longer than 15/20 minutes to get your little one to fall asleep, they're simply not ready. Take a break and try again in 30/60 minutes or when you see the signs again.

But how do you know when they're tired?

Early Signs	Late Signs
Losing interest in play	Getting frustrated
Getting fussy	Arching their back
Going pale	Crying
Staring	Rubbing eyes
Jerky movements	Arching their back
Early Signs	**Late Signs**
Seeking comfort	Rubbing their face on your shoulder
Going quiet	Pulling ears
Staring	Pulling legs up / vigorous wriggling
Red eyebrows	Frustrated rubbing of nose/face

It's always helpful to keep an eye on your child, more than the clock. Try to recognise those tired signs your baby gives you and pop them down for a nap at the earliest cues rather than waiting for the later ones.

If you find it hard or even impossible to recognise tired cues in your little one, it might be useful for you to understand about wake windows.

Let's Talk About Wake Windows

A 'wake window', or 'wakefulness window' is the period between your little one waking and falling asleep again.

Many sleep plans and apps will work on the theory that children have specific wake windows at certain ages. The problem with this is that wake windows are so variable between children so what works for one child, won't work for another.

The other problem with working with set awake windows is that your child's tolerance for being awake changes depending on other variables, not just the length of time they have been awake. Remember that clever hormone adenosine which drives sleep pressure?

The length of awake windows might depend on what activities you've been doing. If you've been to a sensory rich baby class, dazzling your baby with lights and sounds, they may be more tired and have a shorter wake window than if you've had a more relaxed morning at home. They may also have a longer window here if they are overstimulated and need to regulate before they can rest.

Wake windows can also depend on how long they napped for previously, so if they only had a brief nap, they may get tired again quicker, or vice versa!

They can also be impacted by development. If your baby is learning a new skill, let's say rolling as an example, they might get tired more quickly as they are physically more tired, but then they may seem more distracted or harder to settle for naps during this time too!

In relation to temperament, if your baby scored low for regularity then they are highly unlikely to have predictable wake windows.

So, planning your routine around set wake windows can be difficult, and I urge you to only use them very loosely. You can't replace watching and trusting your child's cues with a set wake window in mind.

There haven't been any large-scale studies carried out into wake windows in children, so this is an area that takes some trial and error, and a pinch of salt!

If I'm considering wake windows, I typically only focus on the gap between the last nap and bedtime as I find this has the biggest impact on night sleep.

Age	# Naps per Day	Wake Window
6 – 9 Months	2 or 3	2.5 hours
12 months	2	3 hours
18 months	1	4 hours
2.5 years	1	6 hours

Note I haven't included anything for babies under 6 months, that's because it is even more variable then and it really is anyone's guess!

Wondering Why the Schedule That Worked Now Doesn't?

Remember that sleep is a moving target because as children grow older, their tolerance for being awake gradually gets longer as well. It can feel as though just as you figured it out, something changes, and you need to start fiddling around with it a little bit again.

Try extending the wake window by an extra 15 minutes until you find the time that works again.

Whilst it is important that children nap, try to be reasonably open minded about when and how long for. Many sleep programs you can buy revolve around a 2-hour nap at lunch time, but not all children need really long naps. Their brains are expert at managing what type of sleep they need. The true test is to see what your child's mood is like. If they are generally happy between naps, it is probably working fine for them right now.

One of the common worries parents have with naps is that inevitably their children sleep better on contact; this might be in arms, in a sling, or in motion in the pram or in the car. Contact, motion naps are all fine, still as restorative and I promise you won't be doing this forever – use motion if you need to, especially for the last nap of the day as this is often hardest to get.

Implementing a new routine

When you are starting to implement a new nap routine, especially if you're trying to work towards cot naps, follow the three P's:

Prioritise the location your baby naps best.

Protect the last wake window before bed.

Practice putting them down for the first nap.

Optimise timings – spread naps evenly across the day. Remember it's all about managing sleep pressure across the day to avoid your little one from becoming dysregulated at bedtime.

If you do need to wake them from a nap, try to wake at the end of a sleep cycle to avoid grogginess/grumpiness, look for them stirring or moving for the best time to do this.

Don't stress about having one long nap, some children are cat nappers. If they seem refreshed after their short nap that's OK, and remember, it won't be like this forever!

Troubleshooting Naps

My Baby Wakes When I Put Them Down

How to avoid that frustrating transfer from them being asleep in your arms, to getting them in the cot without waking.

- **Avoid lowering them in on their backs**. This can stimulate the startle reflex and wake them, so try lowering them into the cot on their side before rolling them onto their backs for sleep. Once your baby is able to roll both ways independently, you can leave them to find their own sleep position, but until then it's important that they sleep on their backs as this is safest.

- **Try side or seated settling**. This is where you put baby down sleepy but help them to settle to sleep, resting their side or bottom on the sleep surface with patting or stroking their back.

- **Do the transfer quicker...or slower**. If your little one wakes on transfer after being asleep in arms for a few minutes, the immediate sleep pressure has gone, and it can be hard if not impossible to get them to carry on napping. To avoid this, you can either transfer them as soon as they are asleep (you can try to continue settling in the cot if they do wake) or wait for around 20 minutes in the hope they are in the deep sleep part of the sleep cycle and are less likely to wake.

- **Try a floor bed**. A floor bed can work brilliantly as a way of helping your child to get used to falling asleep on the mattress instead of in arms. You take the mattress out of the cot and put it on the floor, it is important to ensure the space around is safe (i.e., no loose wires, hot pipes or plug sockets etc.). Then you can lie next to your little one cuddling, patting/shushing or whatever it takes to help them to fall asleep. Once asleep you can roll yourself away quietly and no transfer is needed!

My Baby Only Catnaps

- If your little one takes frequent, short naps you can try **to extend awake time** gradually to build more sleep pressure, this can often help to consolidate frequent short naps.

- Try **Rouse to Sleep**. If your little one always wakes after 30 minutes, get in there after about 20 minutes and lay your hand on their chest or arm. The aim is to stir them ever so slightly in the sleep cycle to encourage them to go straight into the next without waking.

- Are they generally happy after a short nap? Or do they still wake after 30 minutes even if they are having contact/motion nap? If so, then the 'short' naps are probably all they need right now.

My Baby Fights Every Nap

- Be objective, are they actually tired? Have they gone past it? If it's a battle, then maybe they just aren't ready yet. Remember the rule of thumb, if they are taking longer than 15/20 minutes to go to sleep then stop trying and watch for tired signs again.

- Review that wake window. Too long will mean they are hard to settle, so check out the averages and compare. Too short a window and they simply won't need to sleep.

- Rule out any hunger / pain / discomfort, or any environmental blocks such as temperature / light / noise.

How Can I Help My Baby to Nap Longer?

Remember that it not always possible to change how long your little one sleeps. But if you find that your baby is grumpy between naps then you may want to give it a try, here are some ideas:

Play around with the wake windows:

- Too short an interval may mean they haven't built up enough sleep pressure to need a long nap.

- Too long awake may mean they've gone past the optimal time for a nap.

Is there appropriate play and connection time between naps?

Try swimming/time on the floor/tickling and silly time. The more physically tired they are, 'could' mean the longer they nap (obviously we are not putting babies through a gruelling boot camp here, just making sure they have appropriate opportunity for stimulation, play and movement).

Try **Rouse to Sleep**. If your little one always wakes after 30 minutes, get in there after about 20/25 minutes and lay your hand on their chest or arm, stroke their face, or rub their chest. The aim is to stir them ever so slightly in the sleep cycle to encourage them to go straight into the next without waking.

Power Naps

Power naps can be a really useful tool when your little one's schedule goes off plan, you have some activities during normal nap times, or when you are trying to first implement a new routine.

A power nap is a nap of 10-15 minutes (no more) which can take the edge off your child's tiredness for a while. They can be especially handy for

- **when your little one wakes REALLY early for the day**, you can use a short power nap to get them through to the more normal time of the first nap. So, for example, if they wake at 5 am instead of 7 am and they normally nap at 9 am then you can do a power nap at 7 am for 10 mins and it shouldn't affect the timing of the usual morning nap too much.

- **when they wake too early from their afternoon nap**, you can use a power nap to bridge the gap to bedtime. It's always better to have a power nap (if possible) and go to bed a little later than to go to bed really overtired. For example, if they wake at 2 pm instead of 3 pm and usually go to bed at 7 pm, you could try a power nap at 5 pm and push bedtime later.

Sometimes trying to fit a power nap in towards the end of the day can be tricky, children don't always conform but it's totally OK to do whatever it takes to get this nap in, so you might need to go out for a pram nap, sling nap or even a drive around in the car.

Dropping a Nap

As children get older, the amount of sleep they need in 24 hours reduces, and the length of time they can tolerate being awake for increases. This means it's an ever-changing routine. As your little one gets older, the number of naps they need in a day will reduce.

When Do Babies Drop Naps?

On average children move towards:

- 4/5 naps by around 3-4 months (evenly spaced throughout the day, AKA your guess is as good as mine!)
- 3 naps between 5-6 months (mid-morning, middle of the day, and mid-afternoon)
- 2 naps between 7-9 months (mid-morning and after lunch)
- 1 nap between 15-18 months (just after lunch nap)

How Will I Know?

You will usually have an inkling when your child is ready to drop a nap as sleep will change. Typical signs of being ready to drop a nap are when they:

- take the nap but then struggle to have the next nap or go to bed.
- don't fall asleep when they usually nap (even with parental support).
- take a lot longer than usual to fall asleep for naps.
- wake up more through the night (this alone is not always a sign, but coupled with the other signs in this list, it might be)
- wake up after a few minutes.

During developmental leaps or these times when you're mid 'sleep regression', it's quite common that babies will refuse a nap (or be harder to settle for naps). If you feel sure they still need a nap, then you might need to work harder than usual! It's fine to resort to car/sling/pram/contact if that's what's needed.

How To Drop a Nap

Now understanding what we have covered about managing sleep pressure until bedtime, how do we get rid of a nap completely without having a long wake window and causing our little one to be over-tired or dysregulated?

Here's how:

For example, let's say your 8-month-old has started to refuse their third nap, or bedtime has started to creep later and later. They seem ready to drop their third nap, right?

The challenge is if you drop the third nap, they will end up being awake from the end of the lunch time nap to bedtime and this is too long a gap!

You can adjust and compensate for this by starting to make the morning nap a little later, as well as the lunchtime nap, and maybe temporarily make bedtime earlier. You can gradually move bedtime later once things have settled.

Old Routine	New Routine
7am Wake	7am Wake
9.30am Nap	10.30am nap
12.30pm Nap	2.30pm nap
4.30pm Nap	7pm Bed
7.30pm Bed	

Remember, dropping naps is not always a linear process. It's fine if they need to have a nap one day, and then not the next. If everything goes a bit wonky, you can always use a power nap to bridge nay long awake periods.

Naps Battles Mindset

Practically every parent I work with is driven round the twist by naps. As adults, we often feel safe with predictability and routine, and a lot of the time, that's not how babies work. A big part of coping when naps aren't going as well as you'd like, or when there just doesn't seem to be any routine is trying to shift your mindset.

Ask Yourself:

Why am I trying to get them to nap now/for longer?

Am I watching the clock rather than my baby's signs?

Am I working to a perceived ideal schedule rather than my child's needs?

Are they crabby/upset between naps? If they are grumpy after waking, is it because they were woken from a deep sleep? Are they still grumpy after a few minutes? If not maybe 'short' naps are fine!

If it's taking longer than 15 minutes to get them to nap, give up as they're not ready. Are they tired or bored/need a change of scenery instead of tired?

Remember, the only thing you can really control about sleep is where they do it (even then sometimes you can't even control that!), so help yourself feel better about it by letting go of the feeling of responsibility and need for control.

Applying the Method

Review and Plan Your Daytime Schedule

Now you know a bit more about what is 'normal', and how the science of sleep works, here is your first practical task.

Create your own sleep plan.

Keep a Sleep Diary – for a few days look for any patterns and note your child's mood between naps, have a think about how easy/hard it was to settle them for naps and bedtime. Copy the template opposite to record the information, it has everything you need to think of.

I find that if you write things down, it is much easier to relate to and understand than if you just look at the same information in an app; try it and see if it helps.

Compare To the Averages – see how your little one compares to the average **sleep in 24 hours** and the average **number of naps**. Are those naps **spread evenly** through the day?

- If your child isn't close to the average, play around with the timings, do they need to be awake a little longer or should they be going for a nap or bedtime earlier?
- Is it time to drop a nap?
- Are they awake for too long before napping/bedtime?
- Are they awake long enough between naps/bedtime?
- Are they having the longest sleep of the day in the middle or second half of the day, if not change it up.

Learn Their Tired Signs – some children are REALLY hard to read. Have a look at the 'Spotting The Signs' section to see some of the less obvious tired signs and watch your little one closely.

When you have completed these steps, you should be able to see where you can make some changes. Try it for a few days to see how your little one copes.

SLEEP DIARY

Make a note of the times your baby sleeps to see if any natural patterns emerge.

Working with your baby's natural pattern will help to make your life so much easier than trying to make them fit into a one size fits all mould.

DAYTIME

Wake up Time _____

Start	End	Duration

Total Day Sleep _____

EVENING

Put Down _____

Fell Asleep _____

NIGHT WAKES

Time	Duration

Total Night Sleep _____

COMPARE TO AVERAGES

What is the average sleep in 24h for this age group? _____

How many naps are average? _____

What is the typical wake window? _____

Is your bedtime routine around 45 minutes? (for babies older than 9m) _____

Is it taking around 15-20 minutes for them to fall asleep? _____

WHAT TO CHANGE

_____
_____
_____
_____
_____
_____
_____
_____

CHAPTER 10

N is for Night times

Remember that Sleep Hygiene is all about creating healthy sleep habits. These chapter is full of tips that will help you make sure your little one is all ready for bed by the time you come to put them down.

Consistent Bed Time

Have an appropriate bedtime; as we saw in the earlier lesson, it's not always realistic that our children will sleep for 12 hours overnight so a 7 pm bedtime may not always work. I tend to find that only when your child is on just 1 nap (or even when they have dropped the nap completely) do they more consistently sleep for closer to 12 hours overnight. Until then it tends to be more like 10/11 hours.

So, by using what you know about wake windows and your bespoke schedule you now have, try to keep bedtime at a reasonably consistent time, or 30 minutes either side.

That being said, and certainly for younger babies who are still napping 2 or more times a day, it's often better to adjust bedtime depending on the time of the last nap rather than risk overtiredness and dysregulation at bedtime by pushing them through to their 'usual' bedtime.

Consistent Bedtime Routine

Have a bedtime routine of no more than 45mins (shorter if younger than about 8 months), this should be from starting the activities you choose to the point they are ready to fall asleep. So, if your little one needs to be asleep by 7.30 pm, you would start your routine at 6.30 pm giving them 45minutes for the activities you decide to include plus about 15 minutes falling asleep time.

Dim The Lights

Dim the lights in the evening; the sleep hormone melatonin is released in dim light so use this to your advantage. Consider dimming the lights a couple of hours before bedtime or drawing the curtains early in Summer. If you find that your child seems super sensitive to light, you can even ask children to wear sunglasses in the early evening.

Keep the lights low especially during bath time and brushing teeth as the bathroom is one of the brightest rooms in the house!

Limit Screen Time

No screens (where possible). Now I am a total realist when it comes to TV and screens, I have two children myself so I fully appreciate the fact that having the TV on can help to distract older children whilst you do dinner or when doing bedtime for the younger ones. If it is working for you, it's fine but if your child is struggling to settle at bedtime, this is one to try out. The blue light from TVs, phones, and tablets can stop that lovely hormone melatonin from being produced.

Consider trying audio books or allowing them to play quietly with some toys in their bedroom whilst waiting for you. We love to switch the TV off after dinner and get out the family board games, jigsaws or colouring books, spending quality time together will help make for an easier bedtime too, leading me nicely onto the next tip.

Focus On Connection

Bedtime is a time of separation from us and often bedtime battles can be a sign that our children need to reconnect with us. You can anticipate this need by setting aside some time for 1:1 play with your little one before you start the bedtime routine. Put your phone down, switch off the TV, stop making dinner or doing other jobs and focus solely on them for at least half an hour. A child who feels secure and connected will be much more compliant at bedtime!

The Sleep Environment

It is helpful to create a space that is not only safe but comfortable and conducive to sleep. Here are my tips for how to do that.

Temperature

An ideal temperature is between 16-20 degrees. Aim for colder bedroom and add warmer bedding, if necessary.

Avoiding hot baths right before bed can help, our body temperature dips at night-time, if we are too warm it is hard to fall asleep.

I don't recommend giving children a duvet before they are about 3 or 4yrs old as they don't always understand that if they get cold, they need to pull it back over themselves. I highly recommend using infant sleeping bags ideally or even sleeping bag suits with feet if your little one doesn't like their feet to be contained.

Humidity

The humidity needs to be above 30%, add a humidifier if needed. If the air is dry, it can dry out our airways which can disturb sleep!

Sleep not Play

Keep the sleep space a calm place for sleep instead of play. If there are toys or half-finished games lying around, tidy them up before going to the bedroom for bedtime. They can be a distraction for children when you want them to be calm.

Red Light

If you're using a night light, swap to a red-light bulb as blue light inhibits melatonin production. Even the light from GroClocks contains blue light so if your little one finds it hard to settle, it might be worth switching it off (to be fair GroClocks won't work for under 2s anyway as they won't understand the concept). There are many lovely red light night lights available to buy online now.

White Noise

Recreate the womb and mask household sounds by playing white noise. You can find this on the online music stores and play it through connected home speakers or tablet devices, or you can but specific white noise machines.

Play it on the lowest volume necessary to disguise sounds, also keep the device as far away from your baby as possible but play it continuously ALL night long. The toys that start playing when the baby stirs or when you switch them on are not as good as by the time the baby wakes it's too late!

Pink noise has been proven to aid deeper sleep so try this when your baby is 6 months or older. White noise is one static frequency like the sound of an out of tune radio, pink noise is variable a bit more like the sound of rustling leaves, waves, or womb sounds.

Dark Room

Make the bedroom as dark as possible. Any light creeping in at dawn can encourage that rise in cortisol, when your little one is coming into a lighter sleep in the mornings which can disturb them and mean they are up and ready for the day! You can buy Groblinds which stick onto the glass and can help to block out more light than just regular blackout blinds and curtains.

In emergencies I have even been known to stick foil to the glass to help!

Bedtime Snack

For toddlers, particularly those who have been in day care and have eaten their dinner early, you could offer a bedtime snack an hour or so before bed. Offer foods that help sleep. Top-up their little tummies with healthy, slow-release energy type foods to fend off any hunger pangs that might disturb them in the early evening. Make sure you choose options that are healthy and not too heavy for little tummies to digest.

Foods that contain tryptophan and magnesium help with melatonin secretion, and complex carbohydrates and protein help to keep little tummies fuller for longer without affecting digestion.

Here are just a few ideas of foods that can aid sleep.

- Eggs – boiled/poached/scrambled.
- Turkey.
- Avocado.
- Porridge with milk.
- Wholemeal toast with nut butter.
- Bananas.

Foods to Avoid

- Sweets and anything high in sugar or additives.
- Caffeine (can be found in chocolate as well as tea/coffee/cola).
- Foods containing high saturated fat.

The Bed

It's a very Westernised, modern idea that babies should sleep independently from parents, in their own room and in a cot.

In many cultures it's normal to bedshare or at least room share throughout infanthood. For example, in Hong Kong, co-sleeping is extremely common, in Japan parents and sometimes grandparents sleep closely with their children until their teens!

For some children, sleeping in a cot alone is too much to bear, they crave the proximity to a parent or dislike the bars as they are a barrier to feeling connected.

It's worth considering whether having your child sleep in a cot is right for them (and you as a family).

A wonderful alternative that is becoming more and more popular is the floor bed.

A cot is great for obvious reasons – your baby is safely contained in there and can't roll out or get up to mischief if they wake in the night, some children like the feeling of security in a smaller space, and like the fact there are sides to lean against. The downside of a cot is that they are a barrier to offering support and comfort without picking your child up, they can be SO hard to transfer your sleeping baby into (especially if you're 'vertically challenged') and some kiddos just don't like them.

Now if you've already purchased a cot that turns into a toddler bed, you could take the side off it and see if that works, if you're worried about them falling out, as a short-term measure you could take the frame away and just go for a floor bed.

A floor bed: think a futon style frame, low to the ground and open on all sides, offers many more options for supporting your child to sleep, settling through the night (you can just get in with them!) and them feeling like they're not trapped (if that's why they don't like the cot)! You may worry that you'll be forever putting your child back in bed if they're free to roam around, however I tend to find when it's just the normal place they sleep, they are not that tempted!

The wonderful thing about the floor bed set up is that you can be lying down next to your little one and once they're settled and asleep, you can stealth-like roll away without disturbing them.

You just need to consider making the room safe, so make sure that there are no loose wires dangling around, any hot pipes/radiators are covered and furniture like wardrobes and drawers are secured to the wall. A floor bed is a brilliant halfway house between co-sleeping and supporting independent sleep.

The Evening Flow

Most parents are aware of the advice to have a bedtime routine.

What do you include in yours? Usually its bath/feed/bed, but I'm going to cover why that may not be the perfect order, and what else you could be missing to help make your evenings and bedtime easier.

I mean, it sounds lovely doesn't it, cuddles, stories a nice warm bath, some milk.... So why do they just seem to hate bedtime? Well, it's not always just because they're trying to annoy us.

Dysregulation at bedtime may come from being over tired, maybe under tired, over stimulated etc., but in addition to that, they can sense our bedtime frustration, their mood feeds off ours so naturally if we are stressed and anxious, they can sense this and it puts them on high alert.

Also, sometimes babies form negative associations with the bedroom, maybe it's because they're not used to being in there much, perhaps it's because bedtimes have been so fraught before that it's not associated with safety and calm (I see this in babies who've previously been sleep trained with cry it out methods) but most often it's because they recognise bedtime as a time of separation.

All these things can make for a difficult hour or so at the end of the day. Planning how you spend the last couple of hours of the day, not JUST the last 30 mins before sleep can really help.

If you want your child to be calm and compliant at bedtime, you are missing a massive trick if you don't lay the groundwork earlier in the evening. Stop thinking 'bedtime routine' and start thinking 'evening flow'.

For me this is the ideal evening flow:

Especially if your child has been at day-care all day, the first thing you'll want to focus on is their basic needs – a snack/dinner, a drink, and the bathroom (when toilet trained). A 'hangry' (angry due to being hungry) or thirsty child will not be in a good mood!

Then they need their connection cup filling back up to prepare for that bedtime separation. One of the best ways to get your little one feeling heard and valued is through play. So, make sure you give them at least 15 minutes of your undivided attention in the evening. Shut your phone somewhere else, ignore the household jobs that need doing for a while and focus on them, let them lead and direct the play and I promise this will help them feel topped up and can massively impact their behaviour for the rest of the evening.

If your little one has some pent-up energy, which can happen after dinner, then you can do some play that will burn off some energy and help get them tired ready for bed. In our house we love to jump on the bed whilst the bath is running, or we do tickle time sometimes too, my daughter Holly loved to be rolled up in a blanket like a sausage roll. For younger babies who are crawling/toddling you can build a little cushion obstacle course to help them move around

Moving the bath to earlier in your evening flow will almost always help make bedtimes easier. I know when we (parents) on the VERY odd occasion get to have a bath, its lovely and relaxing. But let me tell you that for older babies who have discovered the fun world of bath toys and splashing, baths are now stimulating and fun.

The other thing to remember is that they are in the bathroom, which is often the brightest room of the house, it's loud and echoey, both of which don't really go with that need for dim light for melatonin and calm ready for sleep. I so often hear about babies who are happy in the bath and enjoying themselves only to be hysterical and upset whilst getting dry and changed, so if you're doing a bath right before trying to get your little one to sleep and this happens... move that bath earlier.

After an earlier bath, you will then have some time to head back to spend some quiet quality time together before starting the bedtime routine. Here you might read some books, do some jigsaws or colouring, and maybe offer older babies a bedtime snack if needed.

So, for example, if your child needs to be asleep by 7pm, the evening flow may look like this:

17:00   Dinner

17:45   Jump on the bed followed by bath.

18:00   Calm activities e.g., jigsaws/1:1 child-led play

18:15   Start the bedtime routine with a feed.

18:45   Final stories and cuddles ready to go to sleep.

19:00   Fall asleep.

The Bedtime Routine

I cannot overemphasise the importance of having a consistent and nurturing bedtime routine. Not only does it provide your little one with strong cues that it is time for sleep, but it is a time for reconnection with your child on an emotional level. It is important and done well can be a game-changer!

What Should I Include?

As parents, we can be guilty of rushing through the bedtime routine and being distracted and irritable because we are tired and are counting down the minutes before we have our evenings to ourselves! I get it!

However, if you can put together a bedtime routine that you enjoy and you can stay calm and present with your little one, I guarantee things will get easier.

At 6-9 months, the bedtime routine should take around 20-30 minutes. When your child is older than about 9 months, the bedtime routine should take around 45 minutes.

It should be calm and relaxing; it is good to remember that if your child has maybe had a sedentary day or afternoon, they may have some stifled excess energy and will find it hard to settle for bed so that big body play mentioned above is important.

When it's time to start the bedtime routine, you might want to begin with a snack or the last milk feed. This way your little one is topped up but not relying on feeding to sleep when it's time to fall asleep (by the way if you want to feed to sleep that is completely OK so you don't HAVE to do it this way around).

Next you can do the practical tasks – into PJs, wash face and brush teeth, try and do this in a dimly lit room if you can – remember that lovely sleepy hormone melatonin needs dim light... Then into the sleeping bag.

Next you might want to head to the bedroom and spend some time reading some book that you and your baby like. I like to always finish on the same book so that gives a strong cue that it's now time for sleep. If you can, read the stories with a very dim light on, or even using a red light to help keep those sleepy hormones coming.

Some parents like to do grounding activities such as closing the curtains and saying, "Good night, Mr Moon", or saying good night to the toys and pictures around the room. This can be a lovely way to help your baby feel settled and connected to their bedroom.

I also like to do some bridging as recommended by Dr Gordon Neufeld; he talks about bridging the gaps of separation by helping children think about the next point of connection. So instead of 'just' saying "goodnight, sleep tight", you could say "goodnight, sleep tight, I can't wait to have breakfast with you!", this was you're taking their mind of separating from you and shifting it to the next time you'll be together (i.e., breakfast time).

Then you can begin to start settling your baby off to sleep. The chapter A for Associations gives you some different strategies to help support your little one to fall asleep independently in the cot, but it's totally OK if you are happy to rock/feed/cuddle your baby to sleep before putting them down.

Applying the Method

Review Your Evening Flow and Bedtime Routine

So, you now have a daytime schedule that works for your child, and you know more about how to structure your evening well and create a bedtime routine that ticks all the boxes.

Here is your practical Task number 2!

- Review your evening, is your little one's sleep hygiene good? Is there anything you could change?
- Is your evening structured well to include some opportunity for fun, energy release, some time for connection as well as time for practical bedtime activities?

You have now completed two parts of the DNA Method.

Many parents will find that working on the Day and Night foundations alone has a significant impact on sleep.

With that in mind, if you're happy supporting your child to fall asleep by feeding or rocking or whatever else, please do not feel like you must change that at all. You don't.

But if you are ready to change it up then the next chapter is going to help you to do that.

CHAPTER 11

A is For Sleep Associations

Y ou're making a rod for your own back, if you keep picking them up like that!"

How many times have you heard this? Maybe you're even thinking it yourself as you rock your baby to sleep? Are you worried this is it, that you'll be rocking them to sleep forever? This chapter is going to reassure you that you're not doing anything wrong, setting a bad example or making any rods...but it's also going to give you some ideas for how to stop if that's something that is important to you.

What is a sleep association? Is it bad to have one?

Sleep associations are things like rocking to sleep, feeding to sleep, needing to be pushed in a pram or in the car, or thumb/dummy sucking.

A quick note about dummies. Sucking is a very soothing behaviour, if you're concerned about your baby using a dummy, they're safe for use until closer to 4years old. Don't worry about needing to get rid of it urgently. Ideally you would just offer it for naps and night-time sleep, rather than at other times (it can prevent them speaking and noticing hunger cues) but if it seems to work for your baby, then keep it.

If you're at all concerned about the dummy, then it can be easier to get rid of it between 6 and 18 months. Before 6 months, there is some evidence that they can help protect against SIDS. After 18 months you're into toddlerhood and making big changes can be tricker because, well, let's just say toddler know their own minds! Once they're closer to 4 years old it's much easier to negotiate with them!

These are all actions or activities that help our babies to fall asleep. Many babies can't fall asleep without one or more of these cues. It is biologically normal for it to be like this and nothing that you do to help your baby to settle to sleep is bad! You are not making a rod for your own back by rocking or feeding your baby to sleep, nor will you need to do that forever, so please don't worry about doing it and if you are happy to do it, carry on for as long as you want to.

However, many parents I work with get to the point where it's either physically or emotionally too hard to carry on with the current method of soothing, whether that's feeding or rocking to sleep.

What Is Self-Soothing?

As we discussed right at the start of this book, one of the most common goals parents have is for their little ones to be able to fall asleep without too much intervention like rocking to sleep or feeding to sleep. This is commonly thought of as the ability to self soothe.

However, the ability for our brain to truly self-regulate our emotions doesn't properly appear until our twenties. It begins finding 'some' coping skills to do this around 5 or 6 years old when the prefrontal cortex matures. Therefore, it's unrealistic to expect your baby/child to be able to calm themselves down from a state of upset or excitement, they NEED us to help them.

If we are considering 'self-soothing' to be the skill of falling asleep without lots of support, then that might be very possible for some babies.

Back in 1979, Dr Thomas Anders studied two groups of babies overnight, he noted that they all stirred through the night, but some were able to look around, suck their hands and go back to sleep without help and others cried or fussed and needed help, hence the group who fussed were named *Signallers* and some are *Self-Soothers*. Like with the temperament traits in chapter 4, you can't change what your baby is, but you can gently and responsively support them to learn to find other ways to be soothed.

Let's think about it, you have worked on sleep hygiene, you have worked on timing the naps well and you have done a lovely nurturing bedtime routine. You pop your baby in bed and they go to sleep. Did they self soothe? Or were they just nice and calm and ready to go to sleep in a space where they feel comfortable and safe?

We will cover why my strategies never involve leaving your child to cry shortly. We will also discuss the studies that seem to show that Controlled Crying or Cry It Out isn't harmful.

> *"Although many baby sleep trainers claim there is no evidence of harm from practices such as controlled crying, there is a vast difference between 'no evidence of harm' and 'evidence of no harm'."*

Pinky McKay

To Cry or Not to Cry; The Cry it Out Debate

I want to explain why my strategies never involve leaving your baby to cry by themselves or for long periods.

For clarity, I describe what I do (i.e., responsive behavioural modification strategies to aid sleep onset) as sleep COACHING, you'll often hear the term 'sleep TRAINING', and this is usually more linked to the extinction based and non-responsive 'old school' strategies. So that's how I will differentiate between the two from now on.

Let's also consider the definitions of 'training' vs 'coaching'...

Generally, training focuses on the goals rather than the individual needs, and the trainer to trainee knowledge transfer is usually one directional. So, sleep training might be something begun for the benefit of the parents but may not always be age/developmentally appropriate for the child and does not consider the child's needs for a nuanced learning approach.

Coaching considers the specific needs of the individual being coached and then provides tailored direction. So, sleep 'coaching' is about recognising a child's needs and capability and working together on a plan to move forwards that's sensitive to those.

None of this is about making parents feel bad or guilty about their choices and sleep training is a topic many people have extraordinarily strong views about. Let's give you an idea of what these strategies look like and why I personally choose not to use them. I'm here to spread the word that there ARE alternatives to just ignoring your child so that parents don't feel like it's a non-negotiable part of parenting.

You might have heard of strategies like Controlled Crying, Controlled Soothing, Rapid Return, Spaced Soothing, Graduated Extinction, The Ferber Method or Cry It Out.

These methods involve leaving the baby to cry for predefined, set timed intervals before going in to soothe them, for example first every 2 minutes then every 5 minutes then every 10 minutes and so on. If this 'works', the child will gradually accept that nobody will respond to their signals and will just go to sleep. Cry it out is the most extreme form of this, where you put the baby down and don't return at all until the next morning, no matter how much they cry.

These methods are clearly not suitable for children who are already scared of being alone and during periods of normal separation anxiety, and they don't treat the most common sleep problems. For example, this method will not help bedtime battles, night waking, hunger, nightmares, separation anxiety, and they won't cure sleep pathologies like apnoea, snoring, reflux, or night terrors.

So why use them?

What Does the Evidence Say?

My practice is evidence based which means that I look for scientific evidence or actual studies to back up what I'm saying. The problem is on this topic, things can get a little sketchy.

In the interest of being fair and open, there is some evidence (Mindell et al 2006) that children who go through sleep training are:

- less likely to throw bedtime tantrums.
- less likely to wake their parents in the night.
- more likely to settle down within 10 minutes at night.

However, the methods that leave the baby to cry are not the only methods that had similar results (Matthey and Črnčec. 2010) so it is important to understand the potential risks.

Some babies will cry for less time than others depending on their temperament, but a baby who cries themselves to sleep without comfort will still be under emotional stress.

A study (Middlemiss et al 2012) found that infants undergoing extinction training stopped crying at bedtime by night three, but their cortisol levels remained as high as on the first night of training when they were crying intensely. This shows that babies were still experiencing high stress but had stopped signalling, they essentially give up, to preserve energy. This is known as learned helplessness. From the outside, this can seem like it has 'worked' as they no longer cry, however even Richard Ferber who was one of the original founders of this strategy admits that it doesn't teach children to fall asleep.

There has been a study that shows fewer children who have gone through this type of sleep training have a secure attachment although again this study had flaws (Gradisar et al 2016).

There are plenty of studies that show us the effect of cortisol and stress on the brain (Engert et al., 2010), many that look at how important a secure attachment is for children (Schore 2001) but none that say categorically that leaving your child to cry alone is damaging to their long-term health.

Why?

- Controlling the study would be impossible, no family set up is the same, there are different stressors in different homes and babies have such different temperaments.
- It would rely on parents following the process through until it 'worked', and evidence does show that parents find it very difficult to ignore their baby's cries, so lots of parents drop out of these studies.

Margot Sunderland says "An uncomforted child will stop crying eventually if there is no response. But there are real costs.... With what we know about attachment and brain development, responding consistently to your baby's cries is a wonderful long-term investment."

Because there is no guarantee that there is no long-term emotional damage caused, I prefer not to take that risk, especially when there are so many responsive alternatives that can involve no or minimal crying. Fundamentally the strategies you choose to help your child to fall asleep are completely your choice and must fit in with your parenting ethos as well as the urgency you feel to see improvements.

The following section on sleep coaching strategies aims to give you a range of options to choose from and all will focus on being responsive to your child's needs while still giving you the structure to make positive change.

When To Start Sleep Coaching

Deciding to begin sleep coaching is a big step towards change, but is there a right time to do it?

It is always worth remembering, that there is never a time when you can't make positive changes to your child's sleep. It is <u>never</u> too late!

However, there are times when it is perhaps worth waiting before making a start. I would usually hold off starting sleep coaching if your child is going through a development phase (learning to walk, talk, roll, crawl etc.), if they are ill or teething, struggling with separation anxiety or if you are not in the right mindset yourself.

It is often the case when starting the sleep coaching process, that your sleep (at least in the very short term) may get worse before it gets better. So, you need to be prepared for that. We tend to resort to what's easiest to get as much sleep as possible, so you need to be ready for making a change.

Settling Strategies – Where to Start

Now then, you're ready to start to gently change the way your little one falls asleep. But where on earth do you start?

First– work on the D of the DNA Method. Getting up at the same time each day and getting naps working well is half the battle to an easier bedtime settle!

Second – work on the N of the DNA Method, getting that all-important night-time sleep hygiene right will be a gamechanger for a calmer bedtime.

Third – start at bedtime and not nap time. This way you have melatonin, the circadian rhythm and sleep pressure working in your favour; children will accept change much more easily this way.

Be realistic in your expectations when trying to support your little one to fall asleep in a different way. This is not always a quick process, after all you are changing the habit of a lifetime for them.

Of course, with any change, you may meet protest and upset but if you support your child through that time, you can meet their emotional needs whilst still making positive changes.

Crying in the arms of a parent or other primary caregiver who is empathically soothing them is entirely different from crying in a room alone.

When you're starting your journey into making changes, the first few nights can be tough. Partly because we are anticipating it will be difficult. If we are feeling anxious about it, this can rub off onto our children so try to be calm, do some breathing exercises and above all try and think of only the present moment. If you are in the moment, try thinking 'I am comforting my child at this moment' rather than thinking 'I need to get my child to sleep so I can go and make dinner/do the dishes etc' which can be really distracting and unhelpful.

Don't feel like you need to work on your strategy at bedtime and all night long, you don't have to if you don't want to. If you would prefer to just do bedtime, then see how the rest of the night goes that's OK.

Also, don't feel like you must work on naps at the same time, I advise against this as it can all be a bit too much for everyone and we generally find that when night times get better, so do the naps. It's always worth waiting to see.

The Extinction Burst

This is a psychological concept that relates to behaviour. It is something I want to explain as it's an important part of the coaching process and hopefully explains the need for consistency in your approach. It also explains why we sometimes see a blip in the progress when you are trying to make changes.

Burrhus Frederic Skinner was an American psychologist and pioneering researcher in the field of learning and behaviour. Skinner's theory of operant conditioning was that behaviour that is followed by reinforcement will be repeated and occur more often, and behaviour that is not reinforced or is followed by a negative effect will be extinguished.

The extinction burst happens when you remove the consequence to a certain behaviour. Like when your child whines for a treat and you give it to them, when you stop giving the treat anymore, they won't not stop asking for it, but they will ask and scream louder! That is the extinction burst, and when you stick to the new response (not giving the treat), finally, they will stop asking for it.

The same thing can be seen with us and a broken lift. We push the button; the lift door does not open. We don't give up straight away, instead, we'll get frustrated and push the button 20 times (the extinction burst). When we get to see that the lift still isn't opening, we give up, accept futility, and don't push the button anymore.

When thinking about sleep and how to make changes to how your little one falls asleep, you are essentially removing the reinforcement of the behaviour you want to stop.

Taking this to the extreme, this is why Cry It Out is known as an extinction strategy.

In the more responsive strategies that we cover in this book, it is more like when you stop feeding your child to sleep and support them to go to sleep using patting or cuddling instead. They may get upset, but rather than going back to feeding them, you support them emotionally to handle the change. This is a very different approach than just leaving them to cry by themselves, which doesn't help them to manage their emotions, but to just bury them.

You may have tried to change your approach before but been met with crying and protest from your little one. This is why many parents stop trying to make the change and get 'stuck'.

The extinction burst is where your child realises that you are not providing the usual response, so they may protest, and sometimes loudly and for a long time. They'll try to fight the change and may put even more effort into getting the same response as usual (extinction burst). Once the child realises that those efforts are futile, there will be room for them to adapt to the 'new' response.

This burst of emotion can be disheartening but it is a very common response to change. I absolutely don't ever recommend leaving your child to cry by themselves in this situation, but sometimes you need to comfort them through this burst whilst not completely going back to 'square one'.

Dr Gordon Neufeld talks about 'tears of futility' and the essential part they play in how children adapt emotionally. It is SO important for children to feel and express a whole range of emotions, and that they understand what those feelings are.

We become better able to cope with our emotions when we can process them and move forwards. Children often get 'stuck' with certain feelings because they are not allowed space to express them. This might be when parents can't cope with whining or crying, so they tell their child off "be quiet, don't you shout at me" or "why are you crying, stop that", and instead of being addressed, the feeling gets squashed.

Even well-meaning parents can make children squash their feelings, by always trying to prevent upset or disappointment, like when they're not allowed more sweets, instead of empathising with the disappointment (or ensuing tantrum) they give in and give them more sweets!

It's a healthy and important lesson in life to navigate life's losses, upsets, and disappointments by working through those feelings of anger, frustration, and sadness. The way we do that is by encouraging and supporting tears of futility. These tears come when we realise that it's futile to fight/be angry/push anymore.

Empathy is key here, use kind words, soft facial expression and cuddles and love to support them in the change. "Oh, sweetheart I know it's hard when Mummy's boobies are asleep. Let's have a cuddle instead", "I can see how hard it feels for you when Daddy has finished reading the stories, I bet you wish we could read stories all night long! But now it's time to sleep". "I know you love to be rocked to sleep, but you're getting so heavy now I'm going to cuddle you instead, I'm right here".

Remember even if you make a small progression, it is better than none.

Applying the Method

Prepare for Independent Sleep

To properly prepare your child for being able to fall asleep without lots of parental support, you will need to lay some good foundations first.

We will begin by layering up a few different sleep cues and considering introducing a comforter.

Remember, a sleep cue is an action or activity that your baby links with falling asleep. Things like feeding, rocking, patting, singing, humming, and shushing are all common and effective sleep cues that you can do for your baby while they are falling asleep.

It is a good idea to help your baby to become used to having more than one cue to help them to fall asleep as this gives you the option to remove one more easily further down the line. It also means that others can help to get baby to go to sleep if you need a break, or they need to go to day-care.

Layer Up Sleep Cues

Lyndsey Hookway describes this as habit stacking. To do this you simply add in what your baby seems to respond well to, consistently at the start of every sleep (ideally for getting them back to sleep in the night too). Ideally, you would do this for at least 2-4 weeks before moving onto the next step.

Whilst feeding your little one to sleep, you may wish to add in some gentle bottom patting and some shushing, or you may rock, pat, and sing at the same time.

It's good to have a mix of sound and contact cues to help your baby to settle. The sounds cues are in addition to white noise if you're choosing to use that.

Contact Sleep Cues	Sound Sleep Cues
Bottom patting	Humming
Rocking	Shushing
Swaying in arms	Singing
Walking in a sling	Sleep phrase "Its sleepy time now"

Ideally you would spend some time layering up these cues for around 2-4 weeks (ideally 6) so that your baby's brain has got used to these new habits. Then when you're ready to, you can start to remove the cue you're finding hardest to do.

Comforters

Between 6 and 12 months, children are starting to understand that they are separate from the parent, this can be exciting, but they can also feel anxious about it.

Between 8 and 12 months, children might become attached to an item, a toy or blanket for example and this can be a real source of comfort in new situations as well as at naps and bedtime. After about 18 months you may find your child relies even more on the object as this is a peak age for separation anxiety.

If your child does not select an object themselves, you can gently encourage it by always including the item in the bedtime and naptime routine and playing with it lots during the day.

You might choose a toy or a small blanket, but mostly the item will be cuddly and nice to touch. If you can, keep more than one on the go so that if one goes missing, you still have a backup.

If your child is younger than a year old, you can use a comforter whilst helping your child to settle, but it should be removed once they are asleep in line with the safe sleep guidelines of a clear cot being the safest.

Dummies

Sucking is very soothing for babies, so if your little one likes a dummy that's OK, but many parents worry about them. Once concern is about their teeth, the other usually that your baby wakes in the night for it to be replaced for them.

If you find that the dummy helps soothe your child, please have a think about whether you'd rather give your child more opportunities to soothe themselves without you, or to get rid of the dummy.

On good authority from two dentists, if it is gone by around 4 years old, they shouldn't damage their adult teeth.

There are times when it's easier to take the dummy away than others, so if you feel strongly about it then choose your timing. I would say between 6 and 18 months it's easier than before then or later.

Before 6 months if it has been used for sleep, the advice is to keep it until 6 months as it can help with preventing SIDS, and after 18 months you're in toddlerhood and let's just say they know what they want a lot more then!

I personally allowed my son to use his dummy for sleep until he was 4, it was so easy to get rid of it then as we could talk about it and he understood.

If you find that you're having to replace the dummy in the night a lot, you can help your child practice putting it in their own mouth during the daytime. Instead of picking it up and putting it in for them, put it in their hand and take their hand to their mouth.

Once they have mastered this, you can put a few dummies in the cot at night so they can always feel around for one if they wake.

Sleep Strategies

Here are my favourite strategies to help support your child to fall asleep independently.

Gentle Behaviour Modification

This strategy is a combination of an approach called Loved to Sleep from a wonderful book by Andrea Strang and Jen Varela and the habit stacking concept from many other sleep specialists like Lyndsey Hookway.

YAY: This is still a super gentle and baby-led approach. You can change sleep associations without any crying at all from your baby! It generally suits any temperament, especially those who are unadaptable or high needs babies.

BOO: Can take a few weeks, so parents who are already struggling with rocking their baby to sleep might need to be patient. You will need to be fully committed to spending time each night being consistent in your approach.

What To Do

Make sure you have worked through steps D & N of the DNA Method first. This will give you the best chance for things to go well when it is time for your child to fall asleep.

With this strategy, you begin by layering lots of different sleep cues, for example rocking, patting, and shushing. Then when you are ready, start by removing one of the cues. If your baby gets upset, you can switch (or toggle) back to doing the cue you are trying to remove until they are <u>calm</u> then stop it again. The beauty of being able to switch/toggle back to the thing they like is it means there is less upset. I have listed two ideas for how you might work on moving away from rocking to sleep and feeding to sleep.

Moving away from feeding to sleep.

The first mini step in this process is to focus on supporting your baby to fall asleep without sucking, whether that is on a bottle or the breast/chest. How do you do this? I usually suggest two options, the 'Pantley Pull Off' (PPO) and moving the bedtime feed earlier.

The 'Pantley Pull Off'

This is a great option to try, particularly for breast/chest feeding parents, or those who are trying to reduce reliance on the dummy. Defined by Elizabeth Pantley (Author of 'The No-Cry Sleep Solution), this strategy is super gentle, however it can take some perseverance on your part.

Step 1 – begin as always by getting the naps and bedtime timing working well, then add in more sleep cues for at least two weeks. In this example we have been layering feeding with patting and shushing.

Step 2 – Do bedtime as normal. When it's time to start settling your baby to sleep, begin offering a feed, but before your baby is asleep you will break the suction with your finger and remove the nipple/bottle. You may need to gently hold your baby's mouth closed with your finger under the chin to avoid them continuing to try and root. You will then try to settle them to sleep with rocking patting and shushing. If your baby can't settle and they are getting upset, offer the bottle teat/dummy/nipple to calm them and then repeat the removal and pressure under the chin.

Do this as many times as necessary until they can fall asleep without sucking, but with your rocking/patting/shushing.

Step 3 – You would then be able to follow the steps below for moving away from rocking to sleep.

FAQ

How do you know when to remove the nipple/dummy/teat?

Watch for the pace of the sucking slowing down, if your baby is taking a feed and swallowing regularly then you might want to wait for those flutter sucks and the pace slows.

How many times will it take?

Be patient, this can work very well but I have had parents say they needed to repeat this 10/15 times in a bedtime routine, so you might need to hold your nerve and stay calm! All babies are different, and it might be different on different nights.

Moving the Bedtime Feed

This option works well for bottle fed babies (where you don't have the option to keep offering more and more milk until they settle), for parents who find the Pantley Pull Off too frustrating, or where the baby can't cope well with the start stop of the PPO.

Here you will do the feed at the start of the bedtime routine and use the cues you have been layering to settle them to sleep. This can involve a bit more crying so if you need to, offer a feed/a dummy/finger for them to suck to calm then go back to rocking/patting/shushing.

Then when you've been able to get them to sleep with rocking/patting/shushing, you can follow the steps in the next section.

Moving away from rocking to sleep.

Step 1 – begin as always by getting the naps and bedtime timing working well, then add in more sleep cues for at least two weeks. In this example we have been layering rocking with patting and shushing.

Step 2 – Do bedtime as normal. When it's time to start settling your baby to sleep, begin by rocking/patting/shushing but stop rocking as soon as they are calm and comfort <u>to sleep</u> with patting/shushing. If your baby gets upset, then you can 'toggle' back to rocking until they <u>are calm</u> (but not asleep!). When they are calm again, stop rocking and just pat/shush etc until they are asleep. Do this for at least 3/4 days before moving onto the next step.

Step 3 –When your baby is happily falling asleep in arms without rocking, you can try to move onto placing them in the cot and helping them to fall asleep there. So, when your baby is calm after a short time of patting and shushing in arms, pop them in the cot and pat and shush them whilst lying on their side or back. If your baby gets upset here, you can pick them up and pat/shush in arms until calm then pop them back in the cot and continue patting/shushing until asleep. When your baby is happily falling asleep in the cot with just patting and shushing for at least 3/4 days, you can move onto the next step.

Note – you may find it easier to support your baby to sleep at this stage whilst lying on the floor next to the cot with your arm through the bars. If you stand up over the cot, babies often want to stand up too. Lying down can model the behaviour you're trying to encourage.

Step 4 – pop your baby in the cot and just place a resting hand on their chest (or back if they are happier sleeping on their front after they can roll themselves both ways) and shush until they are asleep. If your baby gets upset, you can go back to patting to calm and then go back to resting hand and shushing. When your baby is happy falling asleep like this for at least 3/4 days, move onto the next step.

Step 5 – Pop baby in the cot and sit/lie next to the cot and shush them until asleep. If they get upset, toggle back to the resting hand until calm then go back to shushing until asleep. When your baby is happy falling asleep like this for 3/4 days, move on.

Step 6 – pop your baby in the cot and delay shushing until they demonstrate a need (either by starting to fuss or getting upset). If your baby can fall asleep without any shushing, you may be able to move on to popping them in the cot, saying goodnight and your sleep phrase and leaving. (Please note that I find very few babies are happy with just being left to fall asleep completely alone, lots of babies will prefer you to at least sit with them whilst they fall asleep).

FAQ

What if switching between cues isn't working and baby won't calm?

If your baby is getting upset by moving to the next step in the process, it's OK to pause and go back to what works for the night. Just try again tomorrow.

If this is happening, you might need to spend longer in the current step before moving on to the next, so spend a few more days rocking to sleep before trying to stop it.

My baby is struggling to calm and settle in the cot. I am finding it hard to support them in it too. What can I do?

Consider a floor bed. This way you can offer comfort for them closely without the need for the challenging transfer.

If you have a cot where you can take the side off and turn it into a toddler bed, it can be helpful to do this earlier than you may perhaps have thought you might! This works great for toddlers 14 months and older. I used to kneel by the side of Holly's cot cuddling her to sleep then move away when she nodded off.

The chapter 'Coping with a Crying Baby' may also help with how you manage any crying or feelings of frustration you have during the settling process.

Camping Out

Best for babies 12-18 months, this strategy is about being firm about where your child falls asleep. This can also help children who are struggling with separation anxiety, often they can be hypervigilant about checking if the parent is there every time they wake.

YAY: Can work quite quickly, even within a week. Gives a very clear message about where they sleep, so helps you to keep hold of your boundary.

BOO: Can involve some crying and takes patience and consistency. It can be uncomfortable to sleep in your child's room if there's not enough space, or you can't set up a temporary bed.

What To Do

Make sure you have worked through steps D & N of the DNA Method first. This will give you the best chance for things to go well when it is time for your child to fall asleep.

Be prepared by setting up space where you can be comfortable during the coaching process. I used to have a mattress topper with a duvet rolled-up ready to flip out like a magic carpet whenever I needed it! Some parents have an airbed too.

At bedtime, put your child into the cot calm and (hopefully) ready to sleep.

Lie down next to the cot and offer your usual support like patting/stroking/handholding and shushing through the bars of the cot. Do this until they fall asleep. Your child may get upset and protest, but for as long as you feel comfortable, keep lying down offering support through the cot bars.

By lying down and modelling being asleep next to the cot, you are encouraging your little one to do the same. Often, they will lie down too as they want to be closer to you.

If your child stands up, stay lying down as getting up and physically lying them back down usually only makes the process take longer.

For this strategy to work, you need to be ready to stay with your child until they are fully asleep, and this may take a long time. I usually suggest that you have dinner before you go up and take a drink with you in case you need it.

Ideally, you will sleep in the bedroom with your child all night for at least a week. The purpose of this strategy is to help your little one feel totally confident that you are there with them and they don't need to be hypervigilant and keep waking up to check you are there.

If your child wakes in the night, you can quickly offer reassurance by voice 'Mummy/Daddy is here shhhh', with touch such as patting/shushing.

Eventually, night wakes may reduce because your child is not constantly looking for your presence. When they do reduce, you can just start the night lying next to the cot just while they fall asleep and then leave, and if they wake in the night go back in and lie down next to the cot and soothe them again.

FAQ

Do I need to stay in the room all night?

You can choose to just coach at the start of the night for bedtime, or to carry on and sleep there through the night too. It can work quicker if you choose to stay all night, however I often find that if your child can fall asleep independently at bedtime then the frequency of night wakes reduces quite naturally.

What if they are getting really upset?

We never want our children to get hysterical during the coaching process, this is not good for them, nor is it helpful for getting them to sleep. Check out the chapter on 'What to Do If My Child Is Getting Upset'.

The chapter Feeling Stressed When Your Child Is Distressed will also help.

Bedtime Fading

This is a really good way of helping to implement a new bedtime strategy without lots of protesting. It was developed by Cathleen Piazza and Wayne Fisher as a way of realigning your child's body clock with an earlier bedtime. They were looking at ways parents could support their children in going to bed earlier but of course you can't just expect them to be tired earlier just because we want them to be!

I often use this strategy alongside one of the others. It can help your little one to accept a new way of falling asleep more easily.

This also works well for families where the gap between the bedtime routine and falling asleep takes a LONG time. So, if you're starting the bedtime routine at 6.30pm in the hope they'll be asleep for 7pm but are frustrated that they never fall asleep until 8pm, then this is a good option.

If this happens, the soothing activities you're doing to try and wind them down aren't linked to them falling asleep, so we need to get the two linked again.

YAY: Works on the basis that we wait for the child to be very tired before starting the bedtime routine so the bedtime process is often quick and can often mean a lot less protesting.

BOO: Can risk that they get overtired which can cause other sleep problems, more waking, and early rising so this might not be the right strategy for either very young babies, or those children who are very sensitive to tiredness/dysregulation.

What to Do

Make a note of the time your child usually falls asleep, (not the time you start the bedtime routine, not when they should be asleep but when they usually fall asleep). Then you start the bedtime routine 15 minutes before that time.

For example, if your child usually falls asleep at 9 pm (even if you start the bedtime routine at 7 pm) you would start the bedtime routine at 8.45 pm. The idea is that they are so tired they will fall asleep easily after going through the routine.

When they are falling asleep within 20 minutes of the routine consistently for 3/4 days, you can start to bring bedtime forwards by 15 minutes every couple of days until the bedtime is at a more appropriate time.

Make sure that the activities you do between the old bedtime and the new one are still calm and night-time appropriate, so no TV etc.

Also, if your child is still napping during the day, make sure they don't nap for longer the next day to make up for the later bedtime otherwise nothing will change.

What To Do If My Child Is Getting Upset?

Depending on the strategy you choose, and your baby's temperament, babies will often cry during sleep coaching. Not only is this hard for parents but there is evidence that shows crying that isn't responded to is harmful to babies so is something I always strive to avoid.

I recommend never leaving a child to cry alone for any longer than is absolutely necessary. Except of course in the situation where you are under extreme stress in that moment, and you feel like they are safest by themselves until you can calm down and regroup. If this is the case, leave them safely in their cot and go take some time, we have all been there.

Here are some suggestions for managing crying during sleep coaching:

What type of crying is it? Are they hysterical or are they crying on and off with some pauses for self-soothing?

Hysterical crying should always be responded to quickly but with other types of crying you might decide to take a phased approach to offering support, starting with the least amount of intervention they need.

For example, your response plan might follow this order (but of course mix it up to whatever feels right for you!)

1) Offer sound cues (sleep phrase /shushing / singing / humming).
2) Offer touch cues (hand on chest / patting / stroking / hand holding).
3) Pick them up but hold them still.
4) Hold them and add a bum pat.
5) Hold them bum pat and add rocking.
6) Offer a feed/dummy/finger to suck.

No matter what sleep coaching method you are using it is important that your child does not cry for lengthy periods of time.

If you feel that they are crying too long or too hard (hysterical, screaming) it is always OK to pick them up and comfort them. There's always tomorrow/next week, sometimes they are just not ready!

Tips to help you to manage through the sleep coaching process.

Rest as much as possible when you are able to. The old phrase 'sleep when the baby sleeps' is often overused and underachieved. Often as parents, we feel under pressure to spend nap time doing jobs, taking a shower, or just having some time alone. This is all great but if you are totally exhausted, it is really worth trying to focus on getting some rest whenever you can.

Now I know what it's like, often you find that when your baby finally does go down for a sleep, you're wired and don't feel like you could possibly sleep. BUT hear me out.... studies show that even lying down with your eyes closed can mean your body goes into a light stage of sleep and this can still be restorative. So please take the time to do this, and (unfortunately!) the laundry will still be there when you get up.

If you have a toddler at home with you, I know this feels even more impossible. Could you set up 'movie time' where you get some popcorn or other snacks, grab a blanket, and put on their favourite TV show/film. Even if you're not able to sleep, you can rest. Or arrange a play date with a friend and take it in turns to go for a lie down.

Consider going to sleep when your baby does. Again, I fully understand that this doesn't always feel too appealing, you're desperate to get your evenings back and have some time with yourself or your partner, you're craving some space and freedom. This just needs to be a short-term measure to top up your sleep so that you are better able to handle making the changes you need to make, and not being so exhausted that it's hard to be consistent.

Can each parent sleep in a separate room? It is more common than you may think for couples to sleep in separate bedrooms for a while to maximise sleep. Rather than you both being disturbed every night, and both being exhausted, take it in turns. If you can get at least 5.5 hours sleep, this is proven to make you feel better.

Get in some help. If family can help then great, take any offers that come along and don't be scared to ask. If you don't live close to family, consider paying a doula, babysitter, or night nanny to help.

Co-sleeping. Many families choose to co-sleep when things are tough. There are many ways to ensure you are co-sleeping safely and choosing to do it in a safe way is far better than falling asleep on a sofa or in a chair with your baby. Read more about the recommendations for safe co-sleeping in the chapter 6.

Try to be realistic. In many cases, it is biologically normal for your little one to wake in the night. Often as parents, we project OUR exhaustion onto our children. We think 'oh they must be exhausted, they woke up 3 times last night,' but for young babies and toddlers it is often not a problem for them as they are very well able to cope with disrupted sleep, and of course they nap during the day too.

Know that it will not always be this way. It is easy to say but know in your heart that things will get better, those numerous night wakings will reduce, those short naps will get longer, and you WILL get back to feeling less tired.

There are lots more tips to help you in the All About You chapter, please make sure you read it as it is just as important to focus on you as it is your little one.

CHAPTER 12

Sleep Problem Symptom Checker

You have read through the DNA Method and hopefully now have a good understanding of how to make gentle and positive changes to your child's sleep as a whole picture. But there might be specific challenges that you're experiencing which you just can't make sense of. This chapter will help you to unpick specific problems, why it might be happening and what to do.

Check what common sleep symptoms could show and how to fix them.

Waking soon after falling asleep and one or more times before midnight.

Possible overtiredness, review nap lengths and times or try an earlier bedtime. Not earlier than 6pm though, if they need to go to bed earlier than 6pm, do a power nap, read the section on Power Naps to understand this more.

If your baby is wakeful rather than trying to go back to sleep, they may be under-tired and need a later bedtime/less day sleep.

This can also be developmental, so check if your little one is in a leap or regression period. Have they learned a new skill which could indicate this? Things like clapping, waving, babbling more can impact sleep as well as the more obvious skills like crawling and walking.

Refusing second or third nap

Check if the first nap is too long, anything longer than 90 minutes in the morning is likely to mean they may not be building enough sleep pressure to have another nap. Try cutting the morning nap down by 15 minutes at a time to see if it helps.

Refusing naps can be common during regressions, however, it can also be a sign they are ready to drop one. Read the 'Dropping a Nap' lesson to learn how.

Refusing bedtime

Review the timings. Have you structured your evening well? Plenty of opportunity for exercise and reconnection? Dim lights for 2 hours? Do you need to start your bedtime routine later?

Is your little one going a bit wild? Arching their back, pulling your hair? Rubbing their face on your shoulder? Could you have missed the window and need to bring bedtime earlier?

Waking at 4am

Review environmental causes, this is the coldest part of the night so adding a pair of socks can help.

Does the central heating fire up at this time? Noisy pipes can wake babies as they are starting to come into lighter sleep. Try white noise to mask the sounds.

Is there any light creeping in at dawn? Try stick on black out blinds.

Waking regularly after midnight

Something may be disturbing them when they come into the light sleep stage at the end of each sleep cycle.

Try white noise, check the temperature, and light.

Check for overtiredness, if they fall asleep in 15 minutes or less, review naps and bedtime.

Grumpy after a nap?

If they are woken during the deep sleep part of the sleep cycle, this can cause grogginess and irritability. Sometimes it's better to wait for them to come into a lighter sleep state to avoid this or let them wake naturally.

Waking Hourly

This isn't typical, rule out red flags in Chapter 5, and go back to the basics of sleep hygiene.

CHAPTER 13

Common Early Years Challenges

T here are some common challenging times in the first two years that most parents will need to navigate. Things like separation anxiety, night weaning or moving to their own bedroom. In this chapter, I've got your back – here are my gentle, practical suggestions for overcoming these difficult transitions.

Separation Anxiety

Separation anxiety is a normal period of development and is highest between 8 months and 2 years of age. Peak times for it to feel challenging are 6 months, 8-10 months, 14 months, 18 months, and 2 years.

It begins when your baby understands object permanence (the idea that people and things still exist even when out of view) which can be from 4-7 months old. Your child now realises that you are not there and with no concept of time find this extremely stressful. After all you are their world and their protector, their very survival relies on you!

It's no wonder that your little one gets upset at goodbyes, clingy around strangers and can even start to protest when you leave the room; their Panic/Grief system is programmed to be on high alert for survival. It's also natural for children to cling onto their care giver when they feel unsafe. By clinging on they are trying to calm their arousal system, so please try to go with it as much as you can, it won't last forever and you're not reinforcing it by holding onto them.

Separation anxiety can also affect sleep, especially for naps and bedtimes where they are put to sleep in their bedroom, and you leave as they are so acutely aware of your presence. Separation anxiety is one of the main causes of sleep challenges in the first couple of years.

How to Support Your Child

Practice at home in the day. If you need to leave the room, explain to them that you'll be right back and with some tiny opportunities to practice, they will start to understand.

Always say goodbye. Don't sneak away thinking it will make things easier. If you leave without them knowing this can make them even more alert to you leaving. It's exactly what they're scared of!

Have a goodbye routine, a little ritual that you do the same each time or a phrase that you always say. For example, give them a kiss and say "Mummy/Daddy will be back very soon, have a great time!"

If you are at a large gathering, **allow time to acclimatise them** and follow their lead. If they want you to stay close, do so and you will support them in feeling more confident next time.

For naps and bedtime, make sure you have a **consistent routine that really focuses on connection**. Fill up your little one's love cup and they will feel calmer. If your little one wakes and is happy in their cot, give them a minute or two so they can get used to being by themselves and give them the confidence that they are OK.

If you need to leave them, leave them with someone they know and feel safe and comfortable with. When managing the transition into day care, focus on supporting a new connection with their new keyworker/childminder, even if it's a family member. You can help this by matchmaking – introduce them properly, helping them to understand what your child likes, show your child that this person is safe to be around by looking like you're on the same team as they are.

It is worth considering what type of settling strategy is appropriate during peak times of separation anxiety. Strategies that mean leaving children without a response can heighten the anxiety they demonstrate as it plays exactly into their fears.

Night Weaning

There is no hard and fast rule about whether babies should stop feeding in the night. I believe nobody can tell someone else they are not hungry, and that goes for children too. Even as adults we sometimes wake in the night for a drink, so I try to look at night feeding objectively.

And as with every other part of this course, and parenting in general, all babies are different, and some will want to feed in the night longer than others.

Little ones often feed more in the night during 'regressions' or growth spurts, this is really normal and often they do it because they simply need more calories. They can often want to feed more when they are feeling poorly or teething and having a cuddle and feed in the arms of a parent/carer can help to get them settled and back in bed quickly.

It is also worth remembering that breastfeeding/chest feeding is about so much more than 'just' nutrition, it is about comfort, connection, and closeness. So, when your baby is going through separation anxiety, teething or other developmental leaps they may need to feed more for emotional reasons.

I don't recommend night weaning completely until at least 1 year of age and not before 6 months old, as often all you're doing is taking away the quickest and easiest way of getting them back to sleep. It also goes without saying that if your baby is not tracking their growth centiles, then cutting night feeds is not a good idea.

It's also worth mentioning that night weaning does not guarantee better sleep.

Night weaning is often 'easier' as you get closer to 18 months as you're better able to communicate with your child.

That being said, if your little one is feeding very frequently (for example every 60-90 minutes) or you really just can't cope with it anymore, there are some gentle ways of reducing or stopping feeding in the night.

Start During the Day

Increase the frequency of feeds in the daytime. If your baby has quite long gaps between feeds (say every 4 hours) then consider offering more often.

Optimise feeds during the day. Often babies get distracted during some daytime feeds, so feed in a quiet room with the lights and TV off and close the blinds. You can try wearing a feeding necklace to give them something to play with whilst feeding.

Increase your opportunities for connection. Do loads more cuddles and 1:1 play.

Talk to them about it, read a book to explain – "Nursies When the Sun Shines: A little book on night weaning by Katherine Havener" comes highly recommended.

Simple Ideas for Reducing Night Feeds

Feed at set times. You may for example decide that you will only offer a feed at 11 am and 2 am and settle another way for any other wakes. Or you may say to yourself that you'll only offer a feed for every other wake up.

Gradually reduce the amount you offer. With breastfeeding, this is obviously a bit of guesswork as we don't know how much the baby is taking in, so you might unlatch them a minute earlier than they would usually feed for. With bottle fed babies, you can make bottles up with 1oz less every few days.

Feed Them Up Before Bed Some Breastfeeding Mums feed their baby frequently just on one side in the last couple of hours before bed so the baby gets more high-fat milk and may wake less. If you try this, feed on only on the other breast during the night for the same purpose (Kellymom.com)

Cold Turkey. This is where you just stop feeding overnight, no matter what. Whilst this can be a quick way of doing it (usually it's 3-4 nights of hard work and upset), it's not the gentlest approach and I wouldn't do this for babies less than 18 months, unless there's an urgent reason to stop feeding such as illness.

Gentle Night Weaning

Andrea Strang has written an entire book about her Gentle Night Weaning Process and it is fantastic and works very well. It works on the principle of offering dream feeds instead of waiting for your child to wake with the purpose of breaking the wake/cry/feed cycle.

It works by getting your baby used to having a period of the night without taking any feeds, ideally this period is at the end of the night. This encourages them to have a bigger feed at breakfast time and gets you a nice chunk of sleep at the end of the night when it's often harder to be awake with your baby.

This works very well once you have completed the DNA Method and your baby is able to fall asleep without feeding, that way you will have more success at resettling them without a feed through the night.

Begin by tracking the time of night feeds for a few days, so that you can plan when they get hungry through the night.

Encourage More Feeds During the Day and early evening.

Don't restrict the length or volume of any feeds in the evening, so for any time your baby wakes before midnight, encourage a good solid fed.

Turn the feeds into dream feeds.

Ideally, the feeds will be in quite regular intervals in the first part of the night, continuing a similar timing to how often they feed through the day.

Then offer a dream feed around 30minutes before they usually wake from the time you go to bed. This will involve you setting an alarm to wake up to do it.

Establish a Stretch of Time with No Eating

If your baby can get used to not feeding during the last part of the night, they may stop feeling hungry at this time after a few days. If you have encouraged some feeds earlier in the night, they may be better able to cope with this. Start with a 3-hour stretch (so if they usually wake for the day at 7am, aim for no feeds after 4am)

Work towards dropping a feed.

Once you have got that stretch of time where they don't feed until at least 6 am, you can work on moving the other feeds forward by 15 minutes every few days. When that feed becomes within an hour of the next feed, you can drop it.

For example, if your baby wakes for a feed at 10.30, 1.30 and 4.30am, you'd swap those to dream feeds 30m before. Then settle your baby back to sleep without feeding after 4.30am.

Then to help them gradually get used to a longer stretch without calories, move the latest dream feed earlier and earlier until it's an hour closer to the last feed you did.

Check out the table below for an example feeding schedule. You would stay in each step for 2-3 days before moving to the next.

Bedtime feed	Dream Feed	Dream Feed	Dream Feed
8pm	10pm	1am	4am
8pm	10pm	1am	3.45am
8pm	10pm	1am	3.30am
8pm	10pm	1am	3.15am
8pm	10pm	1am	3am
8pm	10pm	1am	2.45am
8pm	10pm	1am	2.30am
8pm	10pm	1am	2.15am
8pm	10pm	1am	2am
8pm	10pm	1am	
8pm	10pm	12.45am	
8pm	10pm	12.30am	
8pm	10pm	12.15am	
8pm	10pm	12am	
8pm	10pm	11.45pm	
8pm	10pm	11.30pm	
8pm	10pm	11.15pm	
8pm	10pm	11pm	
8pm	10pm		

You may find that you get to a point where your baby wakes after your last dream feed, it's quite possible that they still need a feed for now so if you can't easily get them back to sleep with your usual sleep coaching method, then feed them and try the weaning process again in a couple of weeks.

Please remember thought, that I don't ever recommend night weaning before age 1 to improve sleep because:

1. it's often too hard. Many babies will still need to feed.

2. it's likely they will still wake up through the night, and you'll have to support them to sleep in a different way which will probably feel harder than just feeding them.

You may however find that just reducing feeds can feel like it's a little more bearable, especially if your little one wakes hourly or every couple of hours.

Moving to Their Own Bedroom

Moving your little one from your bedroom and into their own is a big step.

Some parents can't wait to get their bedroom back, and others feel apprehensive that the move will be a nightmare and others feel emotional about it.

Safe sleep guidelines advise you to keep your baby with you for all periods of sleep until they are 6 months old. That doesn't mean that at 6 months you must serve them their eviction notice, but the advice is not to move them <u>before</u> then. It is completely up to you when you decide the time is right after your baby turns 6 months, and don't listen to anyone else's opinion about it, do what's right for you.

That this can feel like a big thing for you and your baby. They have been in your presence almost 24 hours a day since they were born, and it can be a strange feeling for them to find that they are now required to sleep in a room by themselves.

Is There a Good Time to Move Them?

It's not ideal to make big changes like this when your child is going through a developmental period, especially during the times when separations anxiety is high (6 months, 9 months, 12 & 18 months) or if they are poorly, or close to when a sibling arrives.

Apart from that, do it when you're ready to do it. You may find that for a little while bedtimes take a little longer (but they may not!), you might also find that if they are still waking in the night a lot you could find it more of a chore to go to their room to settle them each time (or you might not!). So, you need to be mentally ready for the change.

Prepare Them!

Acclimatise Your Baby You can also prepare by spending some time in the nursery during the day, and even spend a few weeks starting the bedtime routine in there before bringing them back to your room to fall asleep.

Often, we have spent the latter part of pregnancy painting and decorating a beautiful nursery only to find that your baby is in your room for 6 months and you hardly set foot in there. Helping them acclimatise to the room will help. If your baby seems to dislike the cot or bedroom, check out the section 'My Baby Hates the Cot' which covers lots of ways to help.

*Work on the **D & N elements** of the DNA Method first. Starting there you will ensure that by bedtime your baby is calm, tired, and ready for sleep.*

- **Start with bedtime.** When you're ready to go for it, as with any big change, I always start at bedtime. This way you have that lovely melatonin AND sleep pressure in your favour. These two things help children to accept change quicker. You will often find that once they get used to sleeping in their cot at night, they more readily accept sleeping in the cot for naps too.
- **Be consistent.** Keep the bedtime routine as close to what they are used to as possible.
- **Be Present** This can be a big change for your little one, it's understandable if they protest or get upset. It's OK to be with

134

them until they calm and settle, you might even need to hold/cuddle/rock them until they're completely asleep before putting them down. Once this is working well, you might want to start on a strategy to help them to fall asleep independently in their cot. This is all covered in the A for Associations module.

Will It Mean They Wake Less?

Who knows whether they do, or whether it's just that there are less obvious disruptions to our own sleep when we can't hear them as well?

Many people believe that babies sleep better in their own rooms, and without trying you'll never know. One thing I do know, is that our babies will often surprise us so it's if this is an important sleep goal for you, it is always worth aiming high as it might not be as bad as you think.

Try not to feel apprehensive about the move; babies can sense our anxiety so try to be calm when you first decide to move. If you do find yourself feeling upset/angry/anxious at bedtimes, there are a number of really useful calming techniques in the 'Coping with A Crying Baby' chapter.

Moving Away from Co-Sleeping

Many parents find themselves co-sleeping, and it's possible to do this safely by following the guidelines (check out The Lullaby Trust website for more info). Some parents enjoy it and are happy to keep it up, but there are also parents who want their own space back but don't know where to start. Here are some ideas.

- Start with bedtime, any big changes are more easily accepted when we have sleep pressure and melatonin in our favour.

- If you have space, you could work on transitioning to the cot in your own room before moving to a new bedroom if doing both at the same time feels like too much change for your little one.

- If you need to move into their own room and cot at the same time, plan to camp out with your child in their new bedroom until they are used to it, then work on removing yourself gradually.

- Try a floor bed before going straight to the cot. A floor bed can bridge the gap well. You can take the mattress out of the cot and pop it on the floor, making sure the surrounding area is safe (no loose wires, hot pipes, plug sockets etc, and securing furniture to the wall, especially drawer units). Then instead of falling asleep next to your baby on your bed, you would lie next to them on the floor. When they are used to this, you can gradually work on moving yourself further away. You can choose to either pop the mattress back in the cot or keep with the floor bed permanently. If you do, you might want to purchase a frame to help raise it off the floor.

- If you choose to keep the floor bed permanently, don't choose a bigger mattress than a single as it can feel overwhelming for little ones to be in a big space alone.

- Don't feel like it's all or nothing, it's OK to focus on bedtime and then bring your child into your bed later in the night. You might set a rule where you will try to resettle them in their own sleep space until 3am and after that they can come back in with you.

Where Do I Start?

Consider whether you could move into their room and co-sleep there for a while to help them get used to their own space. You may need to do some room acclimatisation here first (see the next section My Baby Hates the Cot/Nursery).

Support them in getting used to having some space between you whilst you are still co-sleeping. Offer a comforter and have that in between you, then gradually increase the space between you through the night.

You may want to use these ideas alongside the settling strategies in the A for Associations lessons.

My Baby Hates the Cot/Nursery!

Does Your Little One Seem to Hate Their Cot or Room? It's not uncommon for babies and children to seem to dislike their cot or room. It might be because it's unfamiliar or because they wake up there and find themselves alone but sometimes children do develop anxiety about the room or even bedtime. If you're anything like me, the nursery was beautifully decorated ready for my baby to arrive only for it to be used as a washing store for the first few months whilst he was in our room with us! So, all too often babies don't spend much time in there.

How can you help your little one start to love their bed, bedroom, and bedtime?

Creating a Sleep Sanctuary!

It can actually be quite simple to help your child to overcome their cot anxiety by making simple changes to the routine and working on your approach alongside some attachment focused activities.

Play

One of the easiest ways to help your little one to get used to their bedroom is to spend some time playing in there, even playing with some toys in the cot.

I would usually recommend that the cot is a space for sleep not play but if your child has some anxiety around the cot this can be a great place to start. You can then gradually reduce the playtime spent in there once they are feeling more relaxed and settled. Do the play sessions a couple of times a day and always stay present, be engaging and fun, and play and interact with them. Start with a short amount of time, take them out of the cot before they get upset, and gradually increase the time you spend playing.

You can work towards leaving them to play whilst being in the same room, but not actively playing with them. If your little one can't even bear to be in the cot for any time at all, start with playing in front of the cot, or even further away first then move towards the cot every couple of sessions.

Time

Just generally trying to actively spend more time in the room will help your little one to get used to it. So, take them upstairs with you and do some jobs such as folding the laundry or cleaning. Think about how it feels for your little one to have moved from your bedroom into the nursery by themselves, especially if you've hardly used it before. By spending time in there with them, you begin to make it a familiar and safe space.

Grounding

A lovely way to help calm stress is to walk around pointing out some of the items in the room, or even say goodnight to things. Doing this calmly can really help to almost distract your little one from any worries they may have, it can also become a consistent part of your bedtime routine!

Attachment Activities

As we have previously discussed, bedtime is a time of separation so can cause anxiety in itself without the worry about the cot/bedroom. If your little one is having these feelings, it is even more important to spend time connecting closely before bedtime. Focused 1:1 play, doing activities that your child wants to do, even putting some family photos around the bed can help, especially if your little one is going through a phase like separation anxiety.

Be Calm Yourself

If you feel anxious about bedtime, your child may be able to sense it, and this can make them feel unsafe. Try some calming strategies for yourself, concentrate on your breathing and try to stay calm and present. Take one bedtime at a time.

My Baby Won't Lie Down!

Sometimes during the coaching process, especially with the strategies where you lie by the side of the cot, your baby will stand up and get upset.

I find that having a battle with them by keeping standing up to lie them back down is unhelpful, everyone gets frustrated, and it can overstimulate them.

A good option is to lie next to the cot and role model the behaviour you're looking for. If you stand over them, they often just want to be close to you so will stand up too, lying down can encourage them to do the same.

Split Nights

Is your baby awake happy and playful for 2 hours? This is a split night.

A split night can be one of those annoying developmental things that happen every so often, I see them happening between 14 and 18 months most often. However, if they happen 3 or more nights in a row and for more than a couple of weeks, it could be a circadian rhythm problem.

When they are not linked to development, split nights happen when the balance and timing of sleep is wrong. So, they often happen when bedtime is too early, or the nap is too long or too late.

Essentially what happens is the circadian rhythm is not aligned with sleep pressure. There is not enough sleep pressure to keep them asleep solidly, so they wake up after a few hours. The problem with this is the sleep pressure is gone and they need to get tired enough to sleep again, which takes a couple of hours.

In an ideal world if they wake up, you would stay in the bedroom and pretend its night-time still, keeping things quiet and dark. That being said, I used to find this quite stressful so there was many a night I would just take Holly downstairs and watch TV for a while until she got tired again!

How to fix split nights

First start by gradually moving bedtime later by 15 minutes at a time, every 2-3 days. Add in a power nap if necessary or move the naps later in the day to help do this without the last wake window being too long.

If you get to a bedtime of 8.30/9pm and they still have split nights, wake them up 15 minutes earlier in the morning every 2-3 days until the split nights stop.

Early Waking

One of the most common sleep problems is children who wake REALLY early in the morning.

As adults it's often the case that our ideal wake up time doesn't match up with our child's. This is because generally children are Larks (they go to bed early and wake early) and adults are often Owls (where we prefer to go to bed later and wake later). If they are waking up after 6am then it's probably a very 'normal' wake up time, although this is admittedly hard for us. You'll find that now you're a parent, 7.30am can feel like a lie in!

However, if they are waking at 4-something or 5-something then this IS classed as early.

Why Are they waking early?

There are a few reasons why children wake early in the morning.

They have simply had enough sleep.

Review the bedtime. If your child is going to sleep at 6.30 pm and only needs 10 hours of sleep overnight, then they are going to wake ready for the day at 4.30 am because they have had enough sleep. This is where it is important to learn how much sleep YOUR little one needs. Remember you can review the averages in the What to Expect sections in the next chapter.

The difficulty here is that their body will be used to this so you will need to adjust the daytime sleep to shift bedtime back. Hard when you're starting the day at 4.30 am! Check out the lesson on Power Naps, these can be a lifesaver as they are a great way to bridge a big wake window without messing up the timing of the next nap. Jump forwards to the last tip on how to get out of the early waking/early bedtime cycle for details on how to do this.

Environmental factors

By the time it gets to 4/5am, Melatonin has almost gone, and cortisol is starting to rise, we also do more light sleep in the sleep cycles at this time of the night. If something in your baby's sleep environment disturbs them, they're going to be easily woken (and it's going to be hard to resettle them now).

Rule out things like light creeping into the room by using blackout blinds and curtains. Try using white noise if you find those pesky dawn birds are tweeting too loudly. If the temperature is cool, could you add socks to their night-time clothes (if or feet are cold, we can't sleep)?

They have gone to bed over tired/dysregulated.

Overtiredness fragments the sleep cycles, especially between 4 and 6am so it can cause early waking.

Review whether the last wake window before bedtime is too long and if it is, bring bedtime earlier, or push the nap later by 15 minutes and see what happens.

Perhaps they need a slightly longer nap?

They have formed a habit wake which needs resolving.

If we repeat something over and over again, it will eventually form a habit. The same thing can happen with night feeding and early waking; hunger and sleep are both linked to our body clock, so to be able to resolve it we need to shift the circadian rhythm.

To do this for early waking, you can use light, sound, and food cues to 'reset' that circadian rhythm. So, when your little one wakes up at 5.30am, you would keep them in the dark and quiet bedroom for as long as possible and you would delay the first feed of the day to a more 'normal' breakfast time.

You might only be able to keep your little one in the dark for a short amount of time before they start getting upset but if you can persevere for as long as possible you should start to see a difference in a few days.

The other thing to try would be the 'rouse to sleep' technique. This can be effective, but of course it means that you need to set your alarm for 15 minutes before they usually wake to gently stir them in their sleep cycle and push them into the next one without waking.

How do we get out of the rut of early wake/early nap/early bedtime routine?

It's so easy to get stuck in an unwanted routine of early waking. If they wake early then typically their whole nap schedule will shift earlier, as will bedtime, and it just becomes the new norm.

To get out of this rut, you can use power naps (little 10/15 minutes naps to bridge the gaps).

For younger babies you can choose to do a power nap at either end of the day, however for older babies, it can be a challenge to get them to power nap in the afternoon, so doing one as the first nap is usually best.

Here's an example where the usual routine has ended up 2 hours earlier because of early waking.

If you continue to do bedtime at 5.30pm, of course they're going to wake early because they've had enough sleep. But just keeping them awake until 7pm or later is also going to be tricky too.

In this example, let's assume you have an older baby/toddler who you know will be hard to nap at 4/5pm.

I would do a power nap instead of the first nap then aim for two 'regular' naps after.

You might find that the first wake window after the power nap is shorter than they can usually manage so follow their cues.

Usual Routine	Early waking routine	How to tweak it
7:00 Wake	5:00 Wake	5:00 Wake
10:00-11:00 Nap	8:00-9:00 Nap	8:00-8:15 Nap
2:00-3:30 Nap	12:00-1:30 Nap	11:00-12:00 Nap
7.30 Bedtime	5:30 Bedtime	3:00-4:00 Nap
		8:00 Bedtime

Alternatively, if it works better you can try for a power nap in the afternoon. This works better for younger babies (probably younger than 8/9 months), but you can also try it if it works better for your day, say if you have a baby class or appointment to get to.

In this example, you may need to cap the second nap to ensure there is enough sleep pressure for the power nap.

Usual Routine	Early waking routine	How to tweak it
7:00 Wake	5:00 Wake	5:00 Wake
10:00-11:00 Nap	8:00-9:00 Nap	8:00-9:00 Nap
2:00-3:30 Nap	12:00-1:30 Nap	12:00-1:00 Nap
7.30 Bedtime	5:30 Bedtime	4:00-4:10 Nap
		8:15 Bedtime

CHAPTER 14

Biologically Normal Sleep in the first Two Years

In this Chapter I want to cover specific age groups, what you can expect as far as development (AKA possible regressions!) and what might be developmentally appropriate behaviour so you're not worried about rods for backs, or what your baby 'should' be able to do.

What To Expect 3-6 Months

The table below shows the averages for babies of this age group. Note the huge range in the average sleep in 24 hours - some babies average 12 hours in 24, others average 15, 3 hours difference!

This information is included to give you an idea of what is common, and not to be used as a 'set in stone' guide of what your baby 'should' be doing. Remember those wake windows, there's no science behind the numbers s these are best guesses, and you are better off relying on your baby's cues.

There are always outliers so try to bear these averages in mind but remember that what YOUR baby's needs may be different. The marker is often in their mood, if they are generally settled and happy between naps then things are probably working well. If your baby seems grumpy then that might be a good indicator that they need some more sleep/shorter times between naps.

Age	Average Sleep in 24 hours	# Naps	Awake Times	Average Day Sleep	Average Night Sleep	Average # Night Wakes
3m	14.4 hours	3 – 4	Variable	5.3 hours	9.1 hours	2.2
6 m	13.7 hours	3	2.5 hours	3.7 hours	9.9 hours	2.5

Paavonen et al. 2020 Normal sleep development in infants: findings from two large birth cohorts. *Sleep Medicine*, 145-154

Potential Sleep Blockers for This Age

4-month FOMO! Babies as they are coming out of the 4th trimester suddenly seem to get FOMO (Fear of Missing Out). The world is now VERY interesting to them. Feeding can often be a challenge as they aren't always able to concentrate. If you're breastfeeding you can try a feeding necklace to keep their focus, or try feeding in a quiet, dark room to avoid distractions.

Naps can also be trickier, partly because of the FOMO, but also around this age, the amount of sleep they need in 24 hours drops quite significantly. It goes from 14-17 hours in 24 at 3 months, to 12-15 hours in 24. So, you may find that cutting the amount of day sleep they are having helps - try capping the day sleep to 3-4 hours and over 3-4 naps.

Sleep may get a little challenging between 4-6 months, often referred to as the 4-month sleep regression. Your little one may start to fight naps more and may start waking overnight more, generally being more unsettled.

The 4-month sleep regression (which can happen any time between 3 and 6 months) is the biggest change to sleep architecture that we go through. There is no going back to how sleep was before, which can be hard to cope with if your little one was sleeping well.... however, after this change there are more ways that you can influence how your baby sleeps.

If you can work on getting some great sleep foundations like the DNA Method in place when your baby is young, then surviving the other sleep regressions can be 'easier' and the great habits you had before will come back again.

Around 12 weeks, 19 weeks, and 26 weeks there might be a fussy period due to developmental leaps (The Wonder Weeks).

Exciting Developments

Babies may roll at this age (so if you haven't got rid of the swaddle by 12 weeks, you need to). Some babies may be sitting up and even crawling!

What To Expect

- More frequent night waking
- Nap challenges
- No obvious predictable routine
- 'Short' naps (30 min naps are very normal)
- Reverse cycling (more feeding at night) due to distracted daytime feeds.
- Your baby may drop from 4 (or more) to 3 naps during this time. Check out the Troubleshooting Naps section for the signs and how to navigate this.

What to Expect 6-9 months

Age	Average Sleep in 24 hours	# Naps	Awake Times (before bed)	Average Day Sleep	Average Night Sleep	Average # Night Wakes
6m	13.7 hours	3	2.5 hours	3.7 hours	9.9 hours	2.5
8m	13.3 hours	3/2	2.5 hours	3.4 hours	9.9 hours	2.4

Paavonen et al. 2020 Normal sleep development in infants: findings from two large birth cohorts. *Sleep Medicine*, 145-154

Potential Sleep Blockers for This Age

It's time to start weaning! Some babies will start sitting independently, rolling, and even crawling.

Common sleep regression around 9 months, linked to separation anxiety and leaps in gross motor development.

Some parents move their babies into their own rooms after 6 months.

Exciting Developments

This is a busy time for babies getting mobile! Rolling, sitting, some babies even crawl, pull up to stand, and some babies at the upper age of this group even learn to walk! Babies are also learning how to feed themselves and are honing their skills for grasping toys, their feet (your hair!). You can support all these skills with plenty of tummy time and play.

What To Expect

- Babies drop from 3 naps to 2 naps (typically by 9 months). Check out the Troubleshooting Naps section for the signs and how to navigate this.

- It's still common that babies wake in the night, in fact it may even increase at this age due to common sleep regressions at 6 and 8-10 months. There is SO much development happening at this age (plus separation anxiety) that your baby's brain is working at maximum capacity, one study showed that only 22% of 8-month-olds sleep through the night (Paavonen et al 2020)
- Separation anxiety can peak around 8-10 months so your baby may need more parental support at bedtime and at nap time and might be 'clingier' during the day.
- You'll start weaning your child onto complimentary foods alongside milk.

Weaning onto Complimentary Foods and Sleep

The current advice for starting to introduce complementary foods is around 6 months; your baby should be able to comfortably hold their own head up, should be able to take and swallow food without forcing it back out with their tongue and should be able to bring food to their mouth by themselves.

Once my baby is on solid food, will they sleep through the night?

Babies don't only wake in the night because they're hungry, so if your little one wasn't sleeping 'well' before starting solids, it may not make any difference. There are a lot of developmental changes going on at this age which can cause babies to wake during the night.

The common first foods that babies try are very low in calories compared to breastmilk or formula so they may even want to feed more in the night, it's important to offer solids as complementary to milk until your baby is 12 months old.

Before 9 months, offer milk first then offer some food 30 or so minutes after to ensure they are still getting enough calories in the day and won't need to catch up with additional feeds during the night.

Allow 1.5-2 hours between dinner and bedtime for their tummies to digest their food; going to bed on a full tummy can make it hard to sleep.

8/9 Month Sleep Progression

Most parents, and parents-to-be, have heard of the 4-month sleep regression, but did you know there are also common bumps in the road at around 6 months and 8-10 months?

- Your baby might need a lot more help to get to sleep for naps and bedtime.
- Night waking may increase.
- Naps might become shorter.
- They're often grumpier, and clingier.

If you're not sure whether a blip in the sleep road might be a regression, take a look at them and think about whether they have learned a new skill. If they have, then that's possibly why you're noticing sleep has got worse.

What is it and why does it happen?

Around this age, babies start to learn to roll, crawl, sit and stand up, all of which they might feel the urge to practice 24/7!

Your baby is also experiencing separation anxiety, so they feel worried and anxious when they can't see you, which can impact how safe they feel being left in the bedroom.

There is also a big jump in language skills around this age. You may notice more babbling and chattering and they may even want to chat during the night.

Also, around this time many babies will drop from 3 naps to 2, and as with any nap transition this can affect night sleep.

It really is no wonder that sleep goes a little wonky for a while!

How long will it last?

Most sleep regressions last 2-4 weeks. That doesn't mean that your baby will go back to how they were sleeping before though. The great news is that once they have passed the first 2-4 weeks, they can often be ready to practice new routines and ways of falling asleep. Perfect timing for the things you are learning in this book.

What can I do?

This is the perfect time to start implementing the DNA Method because routine, sleep hygiene, and consistency will all help.

Review the sleep diary (Task 1) and consider whether it is time to drop a nap.

Accept help if it is offered; these times are tough, and you might feel exhausted and frustrated.

Your baby will go through many of these sleep 'regressions' and some will be tougher to bear than others but try to remember that they are a great sign that your baby developing as they should be!

What To Expect at 9-12 Months

Age	Average Sleep in 24 hours	How Many Naps	Awake Times (before bed)	Average Day Sleep	Average Night Sleep	Average # Night Wakes
8m	13.3 hours	3/2	2.5 hours	3.4 hours	9.9 hours	2.4
12m	12.8 hours	2	3 hours	2.5 hours	10.2 hours	1.8

Paavonen et al. 2020 Normal sleep development in infants: findings from two large birth cohorts. *Sleep Medicine*, 145-154

Potential Sleep Blockers at This Age

Common sleep regression around 8-10 months, often linked to crawling/walking/pulling up to stand and separation anxiety. Big changes with parents returning to work and babies starting day-care.

Some babies are starting day care at this age. This can mean naps are off for a while, and it's common for them to pick up various bugs and viruses for a few weeks.

Exciting Developments

Crawling (even making it up the stairs!), using a pincer grip to pick things up, walk supported or independently, build a tower of blocks, feeding themselves.

What To Expect

- You may find naps naturally get a little longer when they drop to two per day.
- Separation anxiety is high! Expect clinginess and needing additional help to go to sleep at naps, bedtime and through the night.

- 78.6% of babies 6-12 months still wake in the night (Brown and Harries, 2015)
- A few weeks of recurring illness if they start day-care.
- It's still very common that babies need support to fall asleep, so don't worry if they are not 'self-soothing' yet. 50% of 12-month-olds still need support (Goodlin et al 2001)
- It's common for children this age to wake in the night for long periods (a couple of hours or even more), this is known as a split night. See the Chapter on Common Early Years Challenges for how to fix them.

What To Expect at 12-24 Months

Age	Average Sleep in 24 hours	How Many Naps	Awake Times (before bed)	Average Day Sleep	Average Night Sleep	Average # Night Wakes
12 m	12.8 hours	2	3 hours	2.5 hours	10.2 hours	1.8
18 m	12.3 hours	2/1	4 hours	2.1 hours	10.2 hours	1.1
2 y	11.9 hours	1	6 hours	1.9 hours	10 hours	0.9

Paavonen et al. 2020 Normal sleep development in infants: findings from two large birth cohorts. *Sleep Medicine*, 145-154

Potential Sleep Blockers at this Age

Around 14 months and 18 months and around 2years, sleep can go a bit wonky. This is often linked to separation anxiety and needing to drop to one nap.

Exiting Developments

Between 12 months and 2 years there is the biggest boost in language, children are also learning to walk, run, go up and down stairs, crawling into their own car seat, scribble/mark making, using cutlery! Loads of new fun and exciting skills! You will really start to see their personality coming out.

What To Expect

- It's still normal for children to wake in the night. 12-Month-old babies wake on average 1.8 times a night (Paavonen et al., 2020).

- 85% of babies will still wake in the night up to 18 months (Mindell at al, 2010)
- Children often transition from two naps to one during this period, commonly around 16 months.
- It's common for children this age to wake in the night for long periods (a couple of hours or even more), this is known as a split night. See the Chapter on Common Early Years Challenges for how to fix them.

CHAPTER 15

All About You

When we become parents, we inevitably find ourselves falling down the list of priorities. We almost ALWAYS put others first, usually our child (or children), leaving little time or thought about our own needs.

It's important to recognise that you cannot pour from an empty cup and so it is essential that you take time to make sure you are alright.

There's a lot of truth behind the phrase *Happy parent, happy child*. So why do we need to make sure this is a priority and not just a 'nice to have'?

Attainable and Sustainable Self Care for busy parents

The idea of self-care isn't a new thing. We all know it's something we're 'supposed' to do, heck it's forced down our throats all over social media. But how do we practice it when we don't even get 5 minutes to go to the bathroom alone?

Do you feel like self-care is a waste of time, that it won't make you feel any better? Maybe you feel like all you need is a good night's sleep! You might also feel like there's so much on your mental to-do list that sitting down for 5minutes is wasting time? That even if you did manage to get 10 minutes, you'd feel better by getting that next load of washing in, writing the shopping list, or picking up the toys that you keep tripping over?

I hear you, but that's the overwhelm talking. Admit it, you don't really think that doing a quick job is better for you than having a break. Is it your pride telling you that you shouldn't need it, or maybe you don't think that you deserve it?

I can promise you now that if you can find some ways to top up your own needs, you will be a better parent, partner and all round human.

The Secret to Self-Care

For me, it was a couple of things... practice, and giving myself permission to do less.

When you become a parent, you hit the ground running and it becomes hard to stop and rest. Life becomes one fast paced hamster wheel.

When you never stop and rest, filling every spare minute with life admin, household tasks and thinking of everyone else all the time, you get used to running at a high level of energy/stress all the time. Then if you do happen to get 10 minutes to yourself, you can't rest even if you want to, your body can't just switch off that easily. How many times have you thought about having a nice hot cuppa, but then you make it and before you know it, it has gone cold thanks to the 5 jobs you were trying to do instead of just sitting and drinking it?

The only way to get past this, is to practice. Self-care often takes a conscious effort, at least when you're starting out, and this is what makes it even harder to practice.

If you only have 5 minutes, force yourself to take a rest, be mindful in that moment and the more you practice, the easier it becomes. Lots of little breaks will add up over the course of the day or week.

Give yourself permission to do less… You don't have to have a tidy house, home cooked meals, clean hair and all the washing done all the time. That's a big ask for any parent with young children (who doesn't have hired help!). Sometimes (or most of the time) only some of that is achievable! You are not proving anything to anyone by never stopping to take a breath, tell yourself that it's ok to just sit down for a while, say no to that play date or give up on the washing for a couple of days.

Let's change the narrative that parents can have and do it all, we can't! Good enough, is good enough!

What does Self Care mean to you?

The things you think of as self-care need to be the things that you do solely for you, the things that truly top up your own cup. So having a shower, doing the food shop alone, or having an hour to sort the house admin don't count!

Think about the things you used to do before becoming a parent and try to find a way to build this back into your life.

For example, I used to love going to clubs and festivals, I was a regular at gigs and Glastonbury every year. After having kids, I realised I barely even get to listen to my own choice of music anymore (but I now prided myself in my Cocomelon repertoire!).

Now when I have a spare 10 minutes and especially if I'm feeling stressed or tired, I will whack on my favourite singing songs playlist on loud and either go for a walk or dance around the kitchen. I ALWAYS feel better after, and it takes hardly any time at all.

Did you love to get dressed up and look good? Now if you're anything like me, you hardly ever find the time to put make up on or do your hair as there's no time and nowhere to go! Could you focus on taking 5 minutes during nap time using some nice moisturiser on and a slick of your favourite lipstick instead of the household jobs you default to doing first?

Did you love cooking? Now thinking what everyone will eat, every day for what feels like the rest of your life has taken the joy out of cooking? Maybe you could plan and book a dinner or lunch date with a friend, and try out a new recipe while they take care of your baby for a while?

Maybe escaping the house to go to your old yoga class just feels like too big a step? Could you do a 5/10-minute yoga session or meditation instead? Even focusing on your own breathing for 1 minute can help calm your stress levels.

If you can't do it alone, can you practice some of these things with your baby/toddler? They'll love to dance around with you or copy your yoga stretches.

Even 5 minutes of something for you is better than nothing, I promise you'll feel better.

Find your own emotional regulators.

Who are your go-to people who make you feel good? There are energy givers and energy sappers, choose to spend or time with energy givers, those people who build you up, make you laugh, comfort you when you cry, listen to you (I mean truly listen).

Positive self-talk

It's easy when we're overstimulated, overwhelmed, and tired, to be short tempered, frustrated and upset. We might recognise it in ourselves, and it can feel uncomfortable. In these moments choose self-compassion over negative self-talk.

Try to talk to yourself as though you were talking to a friend in the same situation.

Ask yourself what you need in that moment and try to do it.

Notice the feelings you're experiencing and acknowledge them, it can help to breathe deeply, hug yourself or give yourself a massage up and down your arms or even to splash your face with water.

Dr Laura Markham talks about using "your healthy adult self to talk self compassionately to your upset inner child", which I love the idea of.

You could also have some positive affirmations, phrases that you say to help retrain your brain to switch negative thoughts into positive ones. Our brain can get mixed up between reality and imagination, so by repeating positive affirmations we can help to retrain our brains into believing them! Think about what negative phrases you say to yourself and flip them! Phrases like:

"It feels hard because it is hard".

"I am a loving parent".

"Good enough is great, perfect is impossible".

By speaking kindlier to ourselves, we can regulate our emotions better and this is a fabulous skill to teach our children! You can even help them to learn to say affirmations to themselves as they grow.

- ✓ Say them out loud 5-10 times when you wake up and when you go to bed, (saying them out loud is important)
- ✓ Say them and believe them.
- ✓ Be Consistent with them.
- ✓ Be patient, it takes time to reframe your thoughts.

Energy and Eating on Limited Sleep

This chapter was written by Lucy Patel. Lucy is a Registered Nutritionist & Health Coach, and specialises in supporting women regain their health, energy, and body confidence after having children.

She works remotely and from her clinic in Cheshire. You can find out more about Lucy by visiting www.lucypatelnutrition.co.uk.

Eating healthy food, and eating enough of it, can be one of the biggest challenges (other than the sleep deprivation) when you are a new parent, and are experiencing a period of regularly disrupted nights and surviving on a few hours of sleep a night. The last thing you may feel like doing is rustling up a vegetable-packed, nutritious meal; but there are lots of ways you can help boost your nutrition, and your energy, leaving you better equipped to manage the challenges of the day ahead.

A Quick Guide to Your Sleep-Wake Cycle

It may feel like your sleep-wake cycle has a mind of its own now, but even when sleep deprived and experiencing weeks of disrupted sleep, your body will fight to retain its natural pattern of awake and asleep times.

Cortisol, sometimes referred to as the 'stress hormone', has an incredibly important role in our sleep/wake cycle. A 'normal' cortisol pattern sees a rapid increase at around 6am, with a steady decline throughout the day until the evening, when another hormone, melatonin, starts to increase and makes us feel sleepy. Melatonin remains high throughout the night, peaking at around 2am and dropping to its lowest levels at 8am. Therefore, being awoken at 2am-3am can often feel the hardest to rouse yourself and stay awake for a feed or to tend to an upset child, as your sleep-driving hormone is at its most effective.

Sleep deprivation, stress, and hunger

Sleep deprivation can trigger an increase in cortisol as our bodies sense we are in a stressful situation and tries to correct this by providing a surge of cortisol to enable us to 'escape' the perceived stressor. Unfortunately, this response is maladaptive in this case, and only serves to leave us in a more heightened state of anxiety. Cortisol stimulates our appetites and has been shown to increase hunger, driving cravings for sugary, salty, or fatty foods. This is why when you wake up bleary-eyed after a broken night of sleep, the first thing you may want to reach for is a buttery crumpet or the packet of biscuits in the kitchen. This is normal; and whilst the sleep element may be out of your control for the time being, what you choose to eat is within your control, and can be extremely effective in helping to balance out your energy and mood for the rest of the day.

Another hormone, leptin, known as the 'satiety hormone', is impacted by sleep deprivation, having a significantly weaker effect on managing our hunger cues when are not well rested. This can lead to over-eating as our body's usually effective system of telling us when we are full is not working at its best.

So, what can we do about this? The good news is that with a little planning and some small, easy swaps and habit changes, you can give your body all it needs whilst you navigate this wonderful but tricky time of your little one's life.

Snacking

Regardless of how you choose to feed your baby, hunger can hit hard during those night-time feeds. When its 2am and you are exhausted, it can sometimes be hard to distinguish between thirst and hunger, so make sure you always have a bottle of water to hand and have a drink first. If after five minutes you still feel hungry, then a nut-based snack is a great choice.

It is important to have a selection of healthy, tasty snacks right near you, maybe a little snack basket that you ensure stays filled so you aren't caught short. My recommendation is to opt for a nut-based snack which won't spike your blood sugar and will leave you happily satisfied. These are great choices for ready-at-hand night-time snacking that are both delicious and super healthy:

- Deliciously Ella Chocolate Dipped Almonds
- Graze Punchy Chilli & Lime Protein Power
- Nine Bar – Chia & Berries
- Forest Whole Foods Trail Mix
- Popcorn
- Portioned up cheese (think BabyBels or own brand cheeses, or portion up your own in a tub)

It might feel very tempting to pick at sweets or chocolate while your little one feeds, but this will give you a very untimely sugar hit at a time you want to make it as easy as possible to get back to sleep the moment your little one settles.

Daytime Snack Hacks

Snacking can be a great way to maintain your energy throughout the day when preparing a proper meal just doesn't feel feasible for you. In these instances, it is important to ensure you are including protein, fat, and carbohydrates into your snacks to ensure your snacks leave you satisfied. So, how to build a balanced snack when you have 2 minutes (at a push) to make it? Here are six super-quick ideas for you to try:

- Apple slices or oat cakes with peanut butter
- Houmous, tuna or egg mayo on toast with sliced cucumber
- Bowl of full fat yoghurt with some fresh berries
- Cucumber sticks wrapped in sliced ham or turkey.
- Wholemeal bagel with cream cheese and tomato
- Handful of unsalted cashews/almonds and dark chocolate

Power breakfasts for the sleep deprived parent

Here are my top five go-to breakfasts that will give you a great start to your morning and help support balanced energy throughout the day. Starting your day off with a nutritious, balanced meal will reduce cravings and the urge to keep picking at sugary and fatty foods throughout the day, leaving you feeling more energised to keep up with your little one(s). These take anywhere from 30 seconds to 5 minutes to make, so even if you feel you have no time to make breakfast, there is something here for you.

- 2 Weetabix, milk, 1 dessert spoon milled flaxseed, 1 dessert spoon full fat yoghurt, handful of berries.
- Toasted wholemeal bagel with peanut butter and sliced banana.
- Scrambled egg (1 whisked egg, splash of milk, microwave for 90 seconds), piece of wholemeal toast, 4 halved cherry tomatoes.
- Nutty/fruity muesli and milk.
- Porridge (rolled outs, milk, microwaved for 2-3 minutes), with a drizzle of honey and mashed banana or handful of blueberries.

It's all in the planning.

The absolute key to eating well when you have little ones to look after all day is planning; if you don't plan your meals, you will inevitably resort to picking at whatever is around, which usually means lots of high carbohydrate and highly processed foods.

- Sit down one evening and plan out your meals for the next week: breakfast, lunch, and dinner. These don't have to be elaborate, home-cooked affairs; for example, Weetabix for breakfast, a chicken salad sandwich for lunch and fishcakes, potatoes and frozen veg for dinner. The process of writing your meals down alone will move you towards a more

---

committed space, and more likely to follow through with your meal plan.

- Write out your food shopping list; using an app like Recipe Keeper can be helpful here, to save you having to write everything down manually.

- Plan when you will do your big shop, considering when fresh ingredients will pass their Use By date. You may need to top up with a smaller mid-week shop for extra fruit and vegetables.

Cook Once, Feed Your Family for Days

Batch cooking can be a lifesaver when you are sleep-deprived and time-poor. Setting aside one evening a week to batch cook can leave you with ten or more portions of food which are then readily available for lunch and dinner.

The best fuss-free, freezer-friendly batch-cooking recipes are:

- Lasagne and pasta bakes
- Bolognese sauce – freeze in batches and cook some fresh pasta on the day.
- Shepherd's/cottage pie
- Fish pie
- Bean and lentil dishes– chilli con carne, vegetarian chilli, curries

Each of these can easily make 6-8 portions, so enlist some help in the kitchen over a weekend, stock up on Tupperware and fill your freezer with delicious meals.

It can feel hard some days, but making time to ensure you are feeding yourself well, and often, can be a game-changer when dealing with sleep-deprivation and demanding children. Planning and enlisting support from friends and family are crucial in ensuring you look after yourself as well as you look after your little one.

The Ups and Downs of Parenthood

The next two sections are written by my wonderful friend Dr Lindsay McMillan.

Dr Lindsay McMillan is a Clinical Psychologist alongside being a mum to three young children. In her private practice, Lindsay supports parents with their own mental health and emotional wellbeing via 1:1 therapy. Areas of work include anxiety, low mood, depression, stress, self-esteem and confidence, overwhelming emotions such as anger, relationship difficulties, childhood trauma, and attachment. She holds a specialist interest in Parental Gender Disappointment – when the baby is not the sex or gender, very much hoped for.

More information can be found on her website mcmillanpsychology.com You can also find her on Instagram and Facebook @mcmillanpsychology and @theGDpsychologist

Parenting is full of transitions. Just when you get used to one phase with your child, another change comes along. Perhaps you have just had your first baby or multiple babies and have been getting used to becoming a parent. Maybe you have had your second, third, fourth + baby and are now negotiating a new feel to family life. Perhaps you are dealing with the change and hurdles that come as your new-born grows from baby to toddler to young child.

In Jemma's book, you have been learning about expectations for 'normal' baby sleep. This may challenge or confirm some ideas you already have. What is 'normal' when it comes to being a parent and parenting your child or children? Do we all face the same challenges, and should we all deal with them in the same way?

What is 'normal' about being a parent? Spoiler: there is no one 'right' way of parenting.

As a psychologist, I believe that, fundamentally, all parents really do want the best for their children. If I were to ask you what your hopes and dreams were for your child's future, what would you say? If I was answering this for my children, I think I would most like for them to be happy in themselves and to feel loved and secure with those around them.

Although some of us may share common goals, say, for our children's happiness or face similar challenges along the way, parenthood is also a highly individual experience. There is no one 'normal' way to becoming or being a parent. We are influenced by our past, including how we were parented, how we have seen others parent, and our own experiences, such as in our childhoods and our personal journeys to becoming a parent. We are influenced by our current experiences, for example, who we have around us, the support, and opportunities available to us as well as the difficulties and challenges we face, not only in parenting but generally in life as well. We each have our own qualities and values as a person and an understanding of the things that are important to us. The transitions in parenthood constantly challenge our identities, that is our sense of who we are and what is important to us as individuals as well as mothers and fathers.

What do babies and children need from us? (It's a lot!)

One thing that that you will experience as a parent is being responsible for meeting your child's needs. Babies and young children are unable to meet their needs for themselves and so rely totally on their caregivers to meet these needs for them. How responsive and available caregivers are sends important messages to children about themselves, how they can expect others to relate to them and more generally, if their world feels like a safe place or not. It is not about parental perfection; indeed the 'perfect' parent does not exist. There are lots of important lessons our children learn in the moments when we, as their parent, don't get it right and then are able to show and model repair and ways we can try to make our mistakes better.

Let's think for a moment, what do babies, and young children really need? Basic survival and safety needs include being fed nutritious milk/food, avoiding hunger and thirst, having somewhere warm and cosy to sleep and live, hygiene (nappies, bathing), and to be kept safe from the physical hazards of the environment. Babies and young children are wired to maintain proximity to their caregiver and relationships are crucial to the baby. Not only does this increase the chance of having survival needs met, but also relational needs such as comfort, bonding, attachment, and regulation of their developing emotions. When these requirements are generally met most of the time, with a degree of consistency, reliability, and predictability, babies and children are then able to explore their worlds and learn.

Guess what? You have all these same needs too. But are your needs consistently being met now?

You need to be able to eat nutritious food, go to the toilet in peace, shower, or bathe regularly, get enough sleep, exercise, look after your mental health and emotional wellbeing and connect and invest in your relationships with important others such as your partner, friends, and family members. This list isn't exhaustive but is to illustrate and acknowledge that you have physical, emotional, and psychological needs too.

Up to the point of becoming a parent, you maybe had more time and energy to focus on having your own needs met. When children come along and we transition to being a parent, it can feel that the task of nurturing our child becomes all-consuming, often at the expense of nurturing ourselves. Not only that, but the requirements of looking after others means that the pressure on us significantly increases whilst at the same time our own needs often quickly and silently slip down the priority list. In essence, it is very easy for us to fall out of balance, in that our coping resources become reduced whilst we are also trying to deal with increased demands. With small children, self-care can at times feel almost impossible. Even a necessity for some adequate sleep (maybe not even the elusive full night's) may be desperately needed but feel like a distant dream (pun intended).

If this at all is resonating with you, as a mother of three young children, I stand in solidarity with you – slowing down to show yourself care can feel so hard to implement, even when we know it is beneficial and what we need. However, even the smallest acts of self-kindness are better than none.

Here are seven ways to gently check in with yourself and your needs:

1. **Check if your demand vs resources capacities are in balance.** I tend to picture this as like a pair of old-fashioned weighing scales. An exercise I sometimes complete with parents is to write down a list of what they are coping with now (demands) and how they are replenishing their energies (resources). This is often a powerful exercise to visually appreciate any imbalance, and if there is one, the extent of it. For example, the recent lockdowns have meant that many parents have seen some of their resources disappear (such as practical family support or childcare) whilst also managing increased demands (home schooling, furlough, the stress of the uncertainty).

2. **How do you feel and what do you notice you do more of when the demands on you outweigh your resources?** What do you notice in your body? Maybe tenseness or increased anxiety? Heightened feelings of tiredness, exhaustion, tearfulness, even frustration and anger? When you feel depleted do you notice more arguments or maybe having a 'shorter fuse' within your relationships?

3. **If you think of times when you have had adequate resources to cope with life's demands, what benefits do you notice?** How does having time to recharge impact on your emotions, your thoughts, and your actions?

4. **What are the barriers to you investing in yourself currently?** Even when we 'know' something is good for us, it doesn't always mean that is easy for us to do. For example, we may know that regular exercise and healthy eating is great for us, but it can be hard to implement this routinely! What is stopping you right now from regularly making space to nurture yourself? Time, energy, opportunity? Feeling guilty for even thinking about putting yourself 'first'?

5. **Jot down in your phone or on a piece of paper, ways you enjoy investing in yourself, whether these feel realistic or achievable at present.** What did you like doing before you had children? Who would you like to spend time with? If I could wave a magic wand which meant that all your needs could be met, no matter how big or small, what would you wish for?

6. **From your list, where are even the smallest areas of need you can try to meet in your day, with purpose and intent.** Self-care doesn't need to be huge gestures, like a spa day (although how nice would that be occasionally?!). You may need to enlist the help of a partner, family member, or friend for this, especially if you have very young children. Even if it is 10 minutes to purposely have some space on your own to finish a hot drink in peace or a chat on the phone during nap time with a friend, what can you make time and space for? Acknowledging areas of possibility is the first step to making them happen. We might not be able to meet all our needs or meet them in the way we want to but any small acts

of kindness you can show to yourself, on a regular basis can add up and make a difference.

7. **Remember, even in the phases where practical acts of self-care seem impossible, you can still be compassionate and kind with the words you tell yourself.** This is especially important when we are 'running on empty' and feel like we are getting things wrong. Usually when we feel guilt or that we've somehow messed up, it is because we have done something which doesn't align with our personal values. It can be so easy to berate ourselves, which only makes us feel worse and more depleted. Acknowledging the stress, you are under and reminding yourself that you are trying your best can be helpful.

Final thoughts: An important part of parenthood is taking care of yourself too, so that you can deal with the inevitable ups and downs.

Looking after yourself whilst you are fulfilling your role as parent is so important. If it feels like a struggle to do that, to prioritise your own needs occasionally let alone on a regular basis, maybe try to think about smaller ways you can make sure some of your own needs are being met and 'topped up'.

This is like a gift you are not only giving to yourself but one which also, importantly, benefits others around you, including your child(ren). And remember, there is no such thing as a 'perfect' parent, we all sometimes behave in ways that don't really fit with our personal values, especially when we are under stress.

Noticing this and showing kindness and compassion for ourselves, especially when demands outweigh resources is one way to take care of yourself, even more important when the tasks of parenthood limit your ability to use the more practical self-care ways you know will help.

"Really, the primary task of parenting is self-parenting, taking care of ourselves. A lot of other things are also necessary, but that is the baseline."

Dr Gabor Maté

Coping With a Crying Baby

Do you feel stressed when your child is distressed? Coping with overwhelming emotions and unhelpful thoughts when your baby won't stop crying can be very challenging.

In this book with Jemma, you have been Looking at some of the many difficulties parenting a young child can bring such as allergies, feeding issues, and sleep difficulties. Dealing with challenges at that moment, taking time to find possible solutions as well as implementing new strategies takes energy and headspace.

If you are reading this book, it is quite likely that you have been experiencing difficulties with your child's sleep. In my own experience, I know the phases when my children do not sleep well also result in me not sleeping well. Trying to deal with other issues on top of chronic sleep deprivation can be tough and involve a lot of tears (not always just your child's!).

My baby won't stop crying.

I will give you an example from when my twins were smaller. From birth, their different temperaments were evident. I had one generally easy to placate baby and another baby who often seemed uncomfortable, who would cry for long periods of time and be so hard to settle. The longer this went on and the more stress I experienced in other areas of my life, the more I used to dread bedtimes. With a partner working away in the week, I spent hours feeding, rocking, and holding tiny hands through the cot whilst sat on the nursery floor. Looking back, I could have used Jemma's support! I remember regularly feeling upset, stressed, and frustrated when I could not seem to soothe my baby and the crying continued. These feelings, combined with sleep deprivation, would lead me down a rabbit hole of thinking 'what am I doing wrong?', 'what's wrong with her?', 'what's wrong with me?', 'I'm not a good mum', 'I can't stop the crying', 'why is this so hard?', which just made me feel even worse – and so the cycle of overwhelming feelings and emotions continued, feeding in to each other over and over.

Stress Response and the Window of Tolerance

The Window of Tolerance, developed by Dr Dan Seigel, helps us think about the different states we can be in and how our bodies and minds react to stress. When we are feeling calm, collected, able to cope, think rationally, and to regulate ourselves, we are said to be within our 'window of tolerance'. When faced with difficulties and challenges, we may find our natural stress response (flight, fight, freeze) kicks in and we are tipped into a state of distress ourselves – either where we feel like 'shutting down', numb, low, sad, withdrawn, unmotivated, unable to think clearly or 'spaced out' (the freeze response) or where we 'blow up / meltdown', feel anxious, panicked, angry, tearful, upset, have racing or self-critical thoughts, feel on edge or 'high alert' and emotionally overwhelmed (the flight or fight response). These are natural responses we all have to stress and is our mind and body trying to keep us safe from perceived threat or danger (in this case, prolonged periods of our baby crying). Some people's window of tolerance is smaller or bigger than others' and the amount of demands or challenges we can endure before we are triggered into distress ourselves can be affected by our past experiences (such as previous trauma), current general stress (the pandemic has been very stressful for everyone), the support available to us (or perhaps more crucially, not available) and how emotionally balanced we feel in general (the demands/resources scale we talked about in the previous lesson).

It is extremely hard to calm a dysregulated child when we are dysregulated ourselves.

Yet even so, often we must continue parenting and responding to our child whilst we are experiencing the stress response. Some of the strategies we may have used in the past to cope and regulate ourselves (for example, going for a walk to calm down) may no longer be available to us immediately alongside the responsibilities of being a parent. If the overwhelm and stress of an unsettled, non-stop crying baby feels familiar to you, here are seven areas to help you cope with the flight/fight response and get yourself back within your 'window of tolerance' in times of stress.

Seven ways to stay within your window of tolerance:

1. **Notice the physical signs in your body that let you know you are starting to feel stressed.** You may notice bodily sensations such as your heart pounding, feeling hot, flushed, or dizzy, muscles tensing or stomach-churning. This is our body pumping blood to our arms and legs and releasing stress hormones (adrenaline and cortisol). In flight or fight mode, your body primes for action for psychological threat in the same way it would respond to a physical threat.

2. **Notice the feelings that come up for you.** Emotions are never irrational; they can signal that something isn't right and that we may need to take action to look after ourselves or others. Sometimes we can notice certain feelings building up to other feelings. For example, frustration often comes before anger, or you may notice periods of worrying before more intense anxiety or panic. Get to know your own emotions and try to label how you are feeling. What feelings do you notice that

let you know you are building up to the flight/fight emergency mode?

3. **Do something practical.** When you start to notice your stress response kicking in and there is a trusted other available (such as a partner, family member or friend), let them take over for a little while and have a break, even if this is only for a few minutes. If there is no one else around, you can tell yourself you are going to do something now to help you calm and regulate your mind and body.

4. **Use techniques to calm the stress response.** When we are overwhelmed with emotion, it can be hard to think straight and so before we try to do any cognitive work such as challenging unhelpful thoughts we may be experiencing, we need to calm our body down first and regulate our nervous system. Activities that use our senses, slow down our breathing (which may have become shallow and rapid) and bring us back to the present moment can be helpful. For example:

   - **Square Breathing:** Find a square shape nearby, perhaps a window or a cushion. Trace the square with your eyes or hand. On one side, breathe in for four. The second side, hold for four. The third side, breathe out for four and the fourth side, hold again for four. Repeat at least three times.
   - **5-4-3-2-1 exercise:** Find five things nearby that you can see. Four things you can touch. Three things you can hear. Two things you can smell. One thing you can taste. Don't rush through these. Really try to notice the detail around you.

5. **Notice and reframe unhelpful thoughts.** You don't have to just jump into 'positive thinking'. If you notice critical

thoughts (like 'I can't do this', 'I'm a rubbish parent', 'I'm not getting this right'), try to offer yourself a more balanced thought which acknowledges the situation and is kinder and more compassionate. You might like to write some of these alternative thoughts down on paper or in your phone in calmer moments, to access as a reminder when your mind feels 'foggy'.

- **I'm trying my best.**
- **This is hard because it is hard.**
- **Babies communicate through crying, she/he is letting me know how upset they are right now.**
- **We are OK, we are not in real danger, we are safe.**

6. **If you are sleep deprived yourself, please try to rest when you can.** There is a reason why sleep deprivation is used as a form of torture! It has a real impact on our physical and mental wellbeing and reduces our windows of tolerance. 'Books in' time for rest in the day and give yourself permission to slow down, even if just for bursts of a few minutes. Sleep and rest are not luxuries, they are necessities to increase your resource capacity.

7. **Make a plan.** If there is a new strategy you want to try in a situation you know will already be tricky or stressful, try to plan this out and communicate with whoever may be around to help before you are in the situation. When resources are depleted and demands are high, having to cope with additional difficulties or parenting tasks that require a lot of thought and action can add to the stress. Write things down so you don't have to think in the moment. Having a plan, slowing down, and trying some of these techniques may help you respond rather than react in a stressful situation.

Recognising When its More than Being Tired

Even with the fabulous tips and advice you've read about so far in this book, both sleep focused and those from Dr Lindsay, it goes without saying that parenthood isn't the easiest, most fulfilling, happiest time of your life at all times!

Statements like "Enjoy every minute, they're only little for a short time" are unhelpful.

Do you ever feel guilty for not enjoying every moment? Maybe you feel guilty for not enjoying having a baby after you longed for them for so long.

Try not to. Realistically how can you be expected to love every second, when you're exhausted, overwhelmed, and maybe even grieving for your old life before kids?

It is common, natural, and OK to have these feelings at times. But when do these feelings cross over into something more? How do you know when you need more than just 'a good night's sleep' to feel better?

For me it was that nothing could make me feel anything. My kids smiling or laughing didn't stir anything in me, I wanted to cry all the time, I even had visions of driving off the local motorway bridge, I was thinking they'd all be better off without me. I didn't want to play, connect, or show the kids (or Mark) any affection, I just felt nothing but sadness, despair, and absolute full body exhaustion.

Post Natal Depression

According to the NHS website, the main symptoms of post-natal depression (PND) include:

- feeling sad, low in mood or tearful much of the time
- feeling agitated or irritable towards your partner, baby, or other children

- loss of interest in the world around you and no longer enjoying things that used to give you pleasure (like you "cannot be bothered")
- lack of energy and feeling tired all the time, trouble sleeping at night – you may be awake even when your baby is sleeping.
- feeling very sleepy during the day
- problems concentrating and making decisions.
- loss of appetite or overeating (comfort eating)
- negative thoughts such as feeling you are not a good enough mother; you are unable to look after your baby or your baby does not love you.
- feelings of guilt, hopelessness, and self-blame
- feeling anxious that something bad may happen to your baby.
- problems bonding with your baby, no sense of enjoyment in being with them.

Peri-Natal Anxiety

Mind, the mental health charity describes the common effects of perinatal anxiety (PNA) on your body include:

- a churning feeling in your stomach, feeling light-headed or dizzy, pins and needles.
- feeling restless or unable to sit still.
- headaches, backache or other aches and pains
- faster breathing or a fast, thumping, or irregular heartbeat
- sweating or hot flushes
- finding it hard to sleep, even when you have the chance.
- grinding your teeth, especially at night
- nausea (feeling sick), needing the toilet more or less often.
- changes in your sex drive
- having panic attacks.

The common effects of perinatal anxiety on your mind include:

- feeling tense, nervous, or unable to relax.
- having a sense of dread or fearing the worst.
- feeling like the world is speeding up or slowing down.
- feeling like other people can see you're anxious and are looking at you.
- feeling like you can't stop worrying, or that bad things will happen if you stop worrying.
- worrying about anxiety itself, for example worrying about when panic attacks might happen.
- wanting lots of reassurance from other people or worrying that people are angry or upset with you.
- worrying that you're losing touch with reality.
- worrying a lot about things that might happen in the future.
- rumination – thinking a lot about bad experiences or thinking over a situation again and again.
- depersonalisation – feeling disconnected from your mind or body, or like you're watching someone else (this is a type of dissociation)
- derealisation – feeling disconnected from the world around you, or like the world isn't real (this is a type of dissociation).

Many of the symptoms of PND and PNA are common when you are tired, but if they linger, or you experience them on more days than you feel good then please see your GP for support. There is no shame in having PND or PNA, and it's very treatable through talking therapies, self-help, and medication.

To Conclude

In this book I promised to give you a relatable, understandable overview of baby sleep with a process of how to make gentle improvements to try to get better sleep.

How do you feel? Reassured at least, I hope?

Empowered even? Do you feel a bit more confident with more knowledge about it all?

Now you understand the potential impact of your responsive parenting style on the brain and future of your child. You can confidently respond to those suggestions of 'teaching your baby to be independent by leaving them to cry'.

We have covered the science of sleep from birth to 2 years, what you might expect at different ages and phases in your child's development.

Hopefully you'll now recognise that the highs and lows of your child's sleeping patterns are not something to control and micromanage with rigid routines and separation. They are something they can't control themselves and you're not doing 'it' wrong if your child still wakes in the night.

We have considered crying and why the gentle and responsive approach will support your attachment and support long term health benefits for your little one.

You also have a process to follow, the DNA method which gives you a flexible plan where you know the 'easy' things are taken care of first.

Daytimes – well spaced naps are helpful to protect calm bedtimes and night-time sleep quality. There are many things we can try to support daytime sleep for children, but ultimately let go of the need for rigid routines and control. Connection and appropriate stimulation and exercise will support good quality sleep.

Night-times – think of the whole evening flow, not just the bedtime routine. Recognise bedtime as another separation from your child and empathise with their worries about that. Increasing their feelings of connection will be a gamechanger for a smoother bedtime.

Sleep Associations are not bad, it's just that some are easier to manage than others. Personally, my advice is to do whatever it takes to support your child to sleep for as long as you like, only when something becomes unsustainable do you need to change it. It is achievable to change sleep associations without resorting to leaving your child to cry by themselves, and this actually gets easier as your child gets older, and you can communicate with them more easily. Don't worry about supporting your young baby to sleep, there is no such thing as a rod for your back.

We also covered a fundamental piece of the puzzle – you and how you look after yourself. You may feel like you need to put your family first but the saying 'put your own oxygen mask on before you help others' is one to remember in your parenting journey. This of course can sometimes feel easier than others but do make sure that you don't overlook your own needs permanently.

I am aware that there is a wealth of information and ideas contained in the book.

Take a step back and focus on your present experience. The starting point must be your child and yourself.

Try to take a step back from the exhaustion and frustration, anger, embarrassment you feel about how your baby sleeps, try to see them as a tiny person who is learning to exist in a scary new world. Remember that you as the parent have the power to support them in achieving their full human potential, and it all starts in these early years.

With that step back, can you gain any clarity on what might be happening inside them? Ask yourself what are they truly capable of in this moment? Ask yourself, are your expectations realistic today? How can we make a tiny step forward towards that goal which I know often feels so far out of reach.

Be kind to yourself as well as your baby. Re-examine your understanding and expectations and embrace the ideas and practices which feel achievable.

You are unique, as is your baby and there is no right or wrong approach. Parental instinct is very powerful. Don't see this as a battle to be won.

Parenting and sleep behaviours are eternal works in progress. The only certainty is change and the challenges of adapting to it.

In this book I have endeavoured to offer as many options and tools as possible for the positive changes you are seeking but remember one size does not fit all. Try things out but give them 4-5 days before deciding whether it's working or not.

Thank you and wishing you happy days (and nights) and a wonderful and fulfilling parenting journey.

"And so, to sleep...perchance to dream".

William Shakespeare

Recommended Books

Havener, Katherine. Nursies when the Sun Shines. United States, Elea Press, 2013.

Hookway, Lyndsey. Holistic Sleep Coaching: Gentle Alternatives to Sleep Training for Health and Childcare Professionals. N.p., PRAECLARUS Press, 2018.

Kurcinka, Mary Sheedy. Raising Your Spirited Baby: A Breakthrough Guide to Thriving when Your Baby is More ... Alert and Intense and Struggles to Sleep. United States, HarperCollinsPublishers, 2020.

Kurcinka, Mary Sheedy. Raising Your Spirited Child Rev Ed: A Guide for Parents Whose Child Is More Intense, Sensitive, Perceptive, Persistent, and Energetic. United States, HarperCollins, 2009.

Markham, Laura. Peaceful Parent, Happy Kids: How to Stop Yelling and Start Connecting. United States, Penguin Publishing Group, 2012.

Pantley, Elizabeth. The No-Cry Sleep Solution, Second Edition. United Kingdom, McGraw-Hill Education, 2020.

Plas-Plooij, Xaviera, et al. The Wonder Weeks: A Stress-Free Guide to Your Baby's Behavior. United States, WW Norton, 2019.

Strang, Andrea. Gentle Night Weaning for Babies the Kinder Way

Sunderland, Margot. What Every Parent Needs to Know. United Kingdom, Dorling Kindersley Limited, 2016.

Varela, Jen & Strang, Andrea. Loved to Sleep: Nurture Your Baby to Sleep with Minimal to No Crying

Recommended Resources

BASIS – The Baby Sleep Info Source https://www.basisonline.org.uk/

Dr James McKenna University of Notre Dame Mother-Baby Behavioural Sleep Laboratory Safe Co-sleeping guidelines https://cosleeping.nd.edu/safe-co-sleeping-guidelines/

The Circle of Security International Attachment resources https://www.circleofsecurityinternational.com/circle-of-security-model/what-is-the-circle-of-security/

The Lullaby Trust – UK Charity supporting safe sleep https://www.lullabytrust.org.uk/

The Urban Child Institute Baby Brain Development Blog http://www.urbanchildinstitute.org/why-0-3/baby-and-brain

Locate a Tongue Tie Practitioner https://www.tongue-tie.org.uk/find-a-practitioner/

Locate an IBCLC for expert feeding support https://lcgb.org/find-an-ibclc/

References

Anders, T.F., 1979. Night-waking in infants during the first year of life. *Pediatrics*, *63*(6), pp.860-864.

Bohlin G, Hagekull B, Rydell A. Attachment and Social Functioning: A Longitudinal Study from Infancy to Middle Childhood. *Social Development*. Published online February 2000:24-39. doi:10.1111/1467-9507.00109

Bordoni, B., Morabito, B., Mitrano, R., Simonelli, M. and Toccafondi, A., 2018. The anatomical relationships of the tongue with the body system. *Cureus*, *10*(12).

Brown, A., & Harries, V. (2015). Infant Sleep and Night Feeding Patterns During Later Infancy: Association with Breastfeeding Frequency, Daytime, Complementary Food Intake, and Infant Weight. *Breastfeeding Medicine*, 246-252.

Brumariu LE. Parent-Child Attachment and Emotion Regulation. *New Directions for Child and Adolescent Development*. Published online June 2015:31-45. doi:10.1002/cad.20098

Caine, J. (1991) 'The effects of music on the selected stress behaviours, weight, caloric and formula intake, and length of hospital stay of premature and low birth weight neonates in a newborn intensive care unit'. Journal of Music Therapy, 28, 4, 180–192.

Childhood attachment Rees, C., 2007. Childhood attachment. *British Journal of General Practice*, *57*(544), pp.920-922. https://www.ncbi.nlm.nih.gov/pmc/articles/PMC2169321/

Conel, J.R., The Postnatal Development of the Human Cerebral Cortex. Cambridge, Mass., 1963.

185

Črnčec, R., Matthey, S. and Nemeth, D., 2010. Infant sleep problems and emotional health: a review of two behavioural approaches. *Journal of Reproductive and Infant Psychology*, 28(1), pp.44-54.

Cutrona, C.E. and Troutman, B.R., 1986. Social support, infant temperament, and parenting self-efficacy: A mediational model of postpartum depression. *Child development*, pp.1507-1518.

DiTommaso E, Brannen-McNulty C, Ross L, Burgess M. Attachment styles, social skills, and loneliness in young adults. *Personality and Individual Differences*. Published online July 2003:303-312. doi:10.1016/s0191-8869(02)00190-3

Engert, V., Efanov, S. I., Dedovic, K., Duchesne, A., Dagher, A., & Pruessner, J. C. (2010). Perceived early-life maternal care and the cortisol response to repeated psychosocial stress. Journal of Psychiatry and Neuroscience, 35(6), 370–377. doi:10.1503/jpn.100022

Gaertner, B. M., Spinrad, T. L., & Eisenberg, N. (2008). Focused attention in toddlers: Measurement, stability, and relations to negative emotion and parenting. Infant and Child Development, 17(4), 339–363. doi:10.1002/icd.580

Galland BC, Taylor BJ, Elder DE, Herbison P. Normal sleep patterns in infants and children: a systematic review of observational studies. Sleep Med Rev. 2012 Jun;16(3):213-22. doi: 10.1016/j.smrv.2011.06.001. Epub 2011 Jul 23. PMID: 21784676.

Goodlin-Jones, B. L., Burnham, M. M., Gaylor, E. E., & Anders, T. F. (2001). Night waking, sleep-wake organization, and self-soothing in the first year of life. Journal of developmental and behavioral pediatrics: JDBP, 22(4), 226.

Gradisar, M., Jackson, K., Spurrier, N.J., Gibson, J., Whitham, J., Williams, A.S., Dolby, R. and Kennaway, D.J., 2016. Behavioral interventions for infant sleep problems: a randomized controlled trial. *Pediatrics*, 137(6).

Harries, V. and Brown, A., 2019. The association between use of infant parenting books that promote strict routines, and maternal depression, self-efficacy, and parenting confidence. *Early Child Development and Care*, *189*(8), pp.1339-1350.

Hong YR, Park JS. Impact of attachment, temperament, and parenting on human development. *Korean J Pediatr*. Published online 2012:449. doi:10.3345/kjp.2012.55.12.449

Hysing PhD, M., Harvey PhD, A. G., Torgersen PhD, L., Ystrom PhD, E., Reichborn-Kjennerud PhD, T., & Sivertsen PhD, B. (2014). Trajectories and Predictors of Nocturnal Awakenings and Sleep Duration in Infants. *Developmental & Behavioral Pediatrics*, 309-316.

Mark IL, Bakermans-Kranenburg MJ, Ijzendoorn MH. The role of parenting, attachment, and temperamental fearfulness in the prediction of compliance in toddler girls. *British Journal of Developmental Psychology*. Published online September 2002:361-378. doi:10.1348/026151002320620299

Matthey, S. and Črnčec, R., 2012. Comparison of two strategies to improve infant sleep problems, and associated impacts on maternal experience, mood, and infant emotional health: A single case replication design study. *Early human development*, *88*(6), pp.437-442.

Middlemiss, W., Granger, D.A., Goldberg, W.A. and Nathans, L., 2012. Asynchrony of mother–infant hypothalamic–pituitary–adrenal axis activity following extinction of infant crying responses induced during the transition to sleep. *Early human development*, *88*(4), pp.227-232.

Mikulincer M. Attachment working models and the sense of trust: An exploration of interaction goals and affect regulation. *Journal of Personality and Social Psychology*. Published online 1998:1209-1224. doi:10.1037/0022-3514.74.5.1209

Moore, G.A., 2009. Infants' and mothers' vagal reactivity in response to anger. *Journal of Child Psychology and Psychiatry*, *50*(11), pp.1392-1400.

Morgane PJ, Galler JR, Mokler DJ. A review of systems and networks of the limbic forebrain/limbic midbrain. Progress in Neurobiology. 2005;75:143-160.

Moss E, St-Laurent D. Attachment at school age and academic performance. *Developmental Psychology*. Published online 2001:863-874. doi:10.1037/0012-1649.37.6.863

Paavonen, E. J., Saarenpaa-Heikkila, O., Morales-Munoz, I., Virta, M., Hakala, N., Polkki, P., . . . Karlsson, L. (2020). Normal sleep development in infants: findings from two large birth cohorts. *Sleep Medicine*, 145-154.

Peirano, P.D., Algarín, C.R., Chamorro, R.A., Reyes, S.C., Durán, S.A., Garrido, M.I. and Lozoff, B., 2010. Sleep alterations and iron deficiency anaemia in infancy. *Sleep medicine*, *11*(7), pp.637-642.

Pennestri, M. H., Burdayron, R., Kenny, S., Béliveau, M. J., & Dubois-Comtois, K. (2020). Sleeping through the night or through the nights. Sleep Medicine, 76, 98-103.

Picchietti, D. L., & Stevens, H. E. (2008). Early manifestations of restless legs syndrome in childhood and adolescence. *Sleep Medicine*, *9*(7), 770–781. **https://doi.org/10.1016/j.sleep.2007.08.012**

Schore AN. Effects of a secure attachment relationship on right brain, affect regulation and infant mental health. Infant Mental Health J 2001;22:7–66.

Standley, J. M. & Moore, R. S. (1995) 'Therapeutic effects of music and mother's voice on premature infants'. Pediatric Nursing, 21, 6, 509–512.

Thomas, A., Chess, S., Birch, H., & Hertzig, M. E. (1960). A longitudinal study of primary reaction patterns in children. *Comprehensive Psychiatry, 1*, 103–112. https://doi.org/10.1016/S0010-440X(60)80014-4

Wu C huei. The relationship between attachment style and self-concept clarity: The mediation effect of self-esteem. *Personality and Individual Differences*. Published online July 2009:42-46. doi:10.1016/j.paid.2009.01.043